HIGH SPEED IN JAPAN

SHINKANSEN – THE WORLD'S BUSIEST HIGH-SPEED RAILWAY

SECOND EDITION

P.W.B. Semmens
MA, CChem, FRSC, MBCS, FCIT, FILT, FRSA

With photographs by Mikio Miura

© 2000. P.W.B. Semmens and Platform 5 Publishing Ltd.

Published by Platform 5 Publishing Ltd, 3 Wyvern House, Sark Road, Sheffield S2 4HG, England.

ISBN 1 902336 14-3

Printed in England by B.R. Hubbard Printers Ltd, Callywhite Lane, Dronfield, Sheffield S18 6XP.

Foreword

We are delighted to see the publication of this revised edition of Mr. Peter Semmens' *High-Speed in Japan*. The earlier edition was the first book in English comprehensively to cover Japan's Shinkansen, and we have heard that the book was highly regarded and enjoyed great success throughout the world.

The Shinkansen has continued to make remarkable progress since its inauguration, as described in the first edition published in 1997. We have seen various advancements which include the development of new technologies, the introduction of new rolling stock, and the opening of new lines. The Tokaido Shinkansen, the line that stands as a pioneer of the world high-speed railways, continues to progress steadily through the adoption of the latest technologies in all areas. Such progress has been symbolised by the start of operations of our newest Series 700 in 1999. In 2003, we will upgrade all our trains to second-generation rolling stock, which consists of the Series 300 and 700. This will enable us to offer even faster service, and raise the overall efficiency of rolling-stock management. The revised edition of *High-Speed in Japan* provides an interesting and comprehensive description of these recent developments; as in the first edition, it covers the subject thoroughly from the birth of the Shinkansen to its future plans and social impact.

As we start the 21st century, the social and economic situations surrounding high-speed railways are experiencing great changes. In particular, people are becoming more deeply concerned with environmental and energy-related issues. Railways will continue to play an extremely important role as the most environmentally-friendly and energy-efficient mode of transportation in the 21st century.

Geographically, Japan's major cities are linearly located along the coast, thus allowing full use of the characteristics of high-speed railways. This suggests that the Shinkansen is the best form of inter-city transportation for medium- to long-distance travel. On the other hand, cut-throat competition among airlines in the domestic market is considered inefficient. In consideration of energy and environmental issues, it is hoped that they will concentrate on providing international transportation where alternative means are unavailable. We see it as our social mission to further the advancement of the Superconducting Maglev that will introduce a new phase in the progress of high-speed transportation.

This new edition of *High-Speed in Japan* gives the reader an in-depth understanding of the possibilities offered by high-speed railways, and we hope that this book will contribute to the development of high-speed railways throughout the world.

Yoshiyuki Kasai

President
Central Japan Railway

Contents

Front Cover Photograph:
A JR-Central Series 700 Nozomi speeds past Mount Fuji in January 2000.   *Mikio Miura*

Rear Cover Photographs:
Top: JR-West Series 700 Hikari Rail Star at speed on the Sanyo Shinkansen.   *Mikio Miura*

Bottom: JR-East E4 Max in Sendai Depot.   *Mikio Miura*

Author's Introduction

No student of railways anywhere in the world could fail to be aware of the launch of Japan's 'Bullet Trains' in 1964, and first-hand information was eagerly sought from those whose business took them to that country and had been able to experience high-speed rail travel. In 1966 the British Association for the Advancement of Science wished to provide its members with an authoritative account of the new railway, and invited Takeji Hayashi, the engineering member on the board of the Japanese National Railways, to address their 128th Annual meeting at Nottingham. As a member of the Association's Council, I was invited to meet the speaker after his excellently-delivered talk, and subsequently wrote a report on it for *Modern Railways*.

Over the years I remained in touch with Mr Hayashi, who subsequently became President of the Nippon Signal Company, and, when my wife and I visited Japan in 1984, we were very hospitably entertained by him. Twelve years later, when we met again in Tokyo, he presented me with a copy of his autobiography, which included a translation of my article, and it was with considerable regret that we learnt of his death only a few months later.

In the course of my visits to Japan, I have been able to travel in the cab of many different designs of Shinkansen on numerous occasions, as well as their Class 381 electric multiple-unit tilting trains shortly after the Hakubi Line in western Japan had been electrified. In 1982 my wife and I made a private tour of the country after I had visited Osaka to arrange for the National Railway Museum's reproduction *Rocket* to take part in an exhibition there organised by the *Asahi Shimbun* newspaper. Not only did we have the company of a young JNR officer as guide during our travels, but whenever we alighted from a train, the stationmaster, in his cream summer uniform with scarlet hat-band, was waiting outside the door of our coach. After a salute and hand-shake, we were escorted either to our next train or to his office for a briefing on his part of the railway and the community it served. Throughout one could not fail to be impressed with the professionalism of the JNR staff and the enthusiasm they had for the job.

For well over 30 years I have kept myself abreast of Japanese railway developments in general, and those on the Shinkansen in particular, through personal contact and the excellent English-language publications available from railway sources. With Japan becoming steadily more popular as a tourist destination, I increasingly wanted to write an English-language history of the Shinkansen system, and Platform 5 Publishing first enabled me to realise this ambition in early 1997. Later that year I visited the country again, to experience, at first-hand, all those new developments which were then in progress. Three years on there have been numerous changes with the rolling stock used for the Shinkansen commercial services, capitalising on the development work I saw at that time. I thus welcomed the invitation to produce a new edition of this book, to describe some of the changes that have taken place in the meanwhile.

I have also included a chapter on the Privatisation of the Japanese railways, because that is an extremely complicated subject, the details of which are not well understood outside that country. Throughout I have used a capital 'P' for Privatisation, because, at the time of writing, nine and a half years after the status of their railways changed, the government has still not sold all the shares of the new companies that were set up in 1987.

My grateful thanks are due to Mr Yoshiyuki Kasai, President of the Central Japan Railway, for contributing the Foreword to the second edition of this book, in addition to the earlier one.

Although the development of the Shinkansen system is basically a technical matter, the 'Bullet Trains' quickly caught the imagination of artistic photographers. I have been particularly fortunate to have the assistance of one of the present-day exponents of this theme, Mr Mikio Muira, President of Galerie "Trains du Monde" in Tokyo. As well as his own photographs which readers can admire, he has helped me considerably with earlier picture research and advice on many matters. The sources of illustrations are acknowledged individually, except for those from myself or my collection.

In connection with my earlier articles, as well as both editions of this book, I have received help and information from numerous railway officers from the old Japanese National Railways, in addition to those from three large companies that now run the major systems in Honshu - the East Japan, Central Japan, and West Japan Railways. A list of all of them would be far too long to include, and I hope that all those who are not mentioned will consider their efforts and kindness have been adequately reflected in the contents of the book.

There are, however, a number of railway officers whom I must thank by name. Mr. Tatsuhiko Suga, who was seconded to the Japan National Tourist Office in London when I made my first visit to Japan, not only arranged all the travel on that occasion, but we have remained in touch ever since. He is now Executive Director of the East Japan Railway Culture Foundation. In the late 1980s he put me in touch with the General Manager of JR-Central's new London office, Mr Kaoru Umemoto, now the Deputy Director-General of his railway's Corporate Planning Division. Over the years we have had many pleasant times with him and his family in both our countries. He has been followed successively in the London office by Mr. Osamu Nakayama, Mr. Sadaya Kobayashi and Mr. Kunihiro Kondo, all of whom have been invaluable sources of information about railways in Japan. Over the years I have also had many, very helpful, contacts with the recently-retired General Manager of JR-East's Transport and Rolling-stock Department, Mr Yoshihiko Sato. Outside the railways, my grateful thanks are due to Professor Satoru Sone, of Kogakuin University, Tokyo, for much useful advice about Shinkansen technology and practice. Any errors are, of course, my own responsibility.

Japanese railways have long-since been metricated, but the same cannot be said of many of those who read railway books outside that country! I have accordingly used both metric and Imperial units throughout, the order in which they appear and the scale of the conversion being dictated by the context. For those wanting accurate factors, they are included in Appendix 1. Similarly, to enable those interested to make historical comparisons between the different countries' exchange rates, these are given in Appendix 2.

P W B Semmens MA, CChem, FRSC, FCIT, FILT, FRSA, MBCS
Upper Poppleton
July 2000

CHAPTER 1
The Dawn of Japan's Railways

Railways arrived late in Japan. For two and a half centuries the Shoguns had maintained their country's isolation from most of the world, and it was not until they were replaced by the Meiji government in 1868 that a fundamental change took place. Railways were among the earliest proposals made to modernise the country, and the British Minister, Sir Harry Parkes, brought in Henry Brunton, the engineer who had built the first iron bridge in Japan, to advise on railway construction.

The construction of a pilot line between Tokyo, the capital, and the international port of Yokohama was recommended, but initially finance was lacking. In 1869 Horatio Nelson Lay offered to raise the money, but his business methods were somewhat reminiscent of George Hudson's. The Japanese officials saw through his scheming, and proper funding was arranged via the London money market. While this was going on, Edmund Morell took over the planning and construction, moving to Japan from New Zealand, where he had been building railways. The geography and topography of the two countries being similar, he adopted the same gauge as he had used in the Antipodes – 3 ft. 6 ins. (1067 mm).

It is generally accepted that the Tokyo–Yokohama line was the first full-scale railway to be built in Japan, although the city of Nagasaki, some 600 miles away on the western edge of the island of Kyushu, makes a claim that, as early as 1868, it had an eight-mile track along the shore, built by a prominent British merchant, Thomas Baine Glover. The Tokyo line, however, was a much more ambitious project, with a length of 18 miles (29 km), and steam-worked from the start. Surveying started in April 1870, and materials began to arrive from Britain in the following year. The first locomotive delivered was a 2-4-0T from Vulcan Foundry (Works No. 614), and was followed by nine others, plus no less than 58 four-wheeled carriages.

The track gauge of 3 ft. 6 ins. (1067mm) adopted for this first proper railway was subsequently used for most of the Japanese railway network. It was universally employed

Engineering drawings from Richard Francis Trevithick's 1895 paper to the Institution of Mechanical Engineers on the first locomotive he assembled in Japan, a two-cylinder compound. *Courtesy Frank Trevithick Okuno and the Japanese Railway Society*

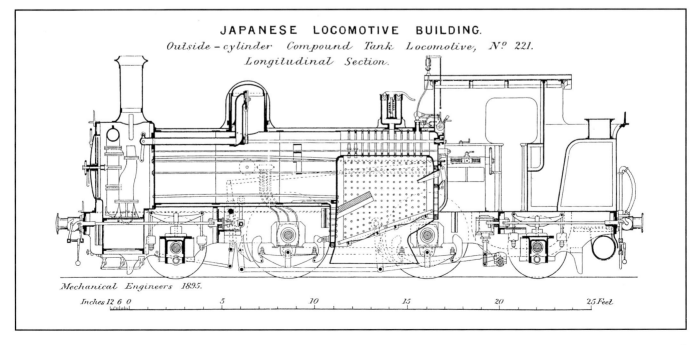

Left: One of the classic paintings of the 1872 opening of the first railway in Japan. *Mikio Miura*

Right: The first locomotive to reach Japan, a 2-4-0T built by Vulcan Foundary (Works No.614), which arrived in 1871. It is now preserved in the Transportation Museum, Tokyo. *Mikio Miura*

Below left: Edmund Morel built the first railway in Japan, but died of tuberculosis at the young age of 30, shortly before the line opened, and was buried in this grave at Yokohama.
Transportation Museum, Tokyo

Below right: Plaque to Edmund Morel at Sakuragicho station, Yokohama. *Mikio Miura*

Two preserved steam locomotives at Modern Transportation Museum in Osaka. Nearer the camera is the Kitson 0-6-0T No. 1801 of 1881, and beyond it is the first locomotive manufactured by Kisha Gaisha, a private company in Japan, 2-4-2T No. 233, dating from 1903. *Mikio Miura*

for the country's national railway system up to the time of the Tokaido Shinkansen in 1964, although several private railways adopted other track widths, including the 4 ft. 8½ ins. (1435mm) 'Standard gauge'. For convenience in this book, I am sometimes referring to 1067mm track as 'Japanese gauge', because the term 'Narrow gauge' is not appropriate and could cause confusion with the numerous light railways that used a gauge of 2 ft. 6 ins. (762 mm).

In June 1872 passenger services began over the first section to be completed, a temporary northern terminus being constructed at Shiodome as the continuation to the permanent Shimbashi station crossed military land. The line had to be rerouted, and this was done in time for the formal opening by Emperor Meiji on 14 October. His personal coach was built in Birmingham, and its Fox bogies from Leeds ran over rails rolled in Sheffield and Barrow. The interior was panelled in walnut, with cushions of Lancashire cotton trimmed in Nottingham lace. British influence could hardly have been more pervasive. As a means of transport it far outstripped its predecessor, the palanquin with its four human bearers, who, at best, managed a mere 20 miles *a day*. Morell died before the line opened, and a bronze bust outside Sakuragicho station in Yokohama commemorates his pioneering work. His Japanese wife died less than a year later, but was able to see the completion of the work.

Other British engineers contributed significantly to the subsequent development of the Japanese railway network, among them two grandsons of Richard Trevithick, the Cornish pioneer whose cumbersome geared locomotive had lumbered down the Penydarren Tramway in South Wales in 1804. Although he died in straitened circumstances, many of his descendants held significant positions of responsibility on railways throughout the world. It was Richard Francis Trevithick who supervised the assembly of the first locomotive in Japan at Kobe in 1893, but two further years were to elapse before the rise of other Japanese heavy industries enabled one to be built wholly from native components. Even so, by 1911 1023 British-built steam locomotives had been supplied to Japan, one North British order in 1899 being for no less than 268 machines.

To complement the mechanical engineering expertise of Richard Francis, one of his brothers – Francis Henry –had arrived in 1877. He was a civil engineer, and was involved in the construction of considerable lengths of railway in Japan. Both of them married Japanese wives, and in 1916 Francis Henry's eldest son became the noted captain of a liner plying between Yokohama and London. One of his sons, Frank Trevithick Okuno, lives in London, and is active in the pending celebrations of the bicentenary of Richard Trevithick's road engine.

2-4-2T No. 137, the first locomotive constructed in Japan. It was assembled by R.F. Trevithick at Kobe Locomotive Works in October 1892. This class later became known as JNR series 860.
Transportation Museum, Tokyo

CHAPTER 2

Structure of Japan's Railway System

This is a book about the late-twentieth-century Shinkansen high-speed lines, so it is not appropriate to describe the growth of the Japanese railway system in detail, but the dates of some of the historical highlights can be found in the Chronology, together with a reference for further reading. It is nevertheless necessary to fill in some of the background that followed the opening of that country's first line in 1872. However, before doing that, we must take a look at Japan's geography, because this has had a fundamental influence on its railways.

The area of Japan is some 50% greater than that of the United Kingdom, but much of the country is mountainous, and less than a fifth of the land surface is habitable. By European standards Japan's mountains are geologically 'young', and this presents the civil engineers with many problems. The country consists of four main islands, the largest being Honshu. At its western end is Kyushu, with Shikoku off the southern coast, and Hokkaido to the north. Some 3900 smaller islands dot the surrounding waters. The population of 125 million – more than twice our own – is thus crowded into the coastal plains, the largest of which is around Tokyo, where 11.5 million live in the inner metropolitan area, with another 2.9 million in Yokohama.

Westwards along the Tokaido corridor lie the cities of Nagoya (2.1 million), Kyoto (1.4 million), Osaka (2.5 million) and Kobe (1.5 million), and this area encompasses the country's main governing, financial, cultural and manufacturing centres. It is not surprising that the Tokaido Line was the first major trunk route to be completed, the tracks being built from the original Tokyo and Kobe railheads at opposite ends. Through services over this 367-mile (590 km) route began in July 1889, the journey taking just under 20 hours. By 1896 the timings had been reduced to a little over 17 hours, and lightweight 'Super Expresses' cut this to 13hr 40 min in 1906. By this time the route was also an important freight artery, connecting Tokyo with Shimonoseki, the port used as the railhead for coal and steel produced in Kyushu, Korea and China.

It was not until 1913 that the route became double-track throughout. Electric traction began in Japan in a modest way in 1895, but by 1956 the Tokaido Line had been completely electrified. This was in spite of the ravages of the Pacific War, when the Japanese railways were extensively bombed, while those near the coast were bombarded by battleships. Even so, by 1964, when the Tokaido Shinkansen opened, the best timing by the 343 mile (553 km) classic route between Tokyo and Osaka was 6½ hours, far too long to encourage many people to make return business trips within a day by rail.

Many of the first railways in Japan had been built privately, but in 1906 the nationalisation of the main lines began, forming the 4445-mile (7153 km) Japanese Imperial Railways, although 446 miles (717km) of urban lines remained in private hands. In 1892 an act had provided for an extensive national system, and building of new 'Japanese-gauge' lines continued up to World War II. After a rapid boost in route mileage from 1593 to 4543 (2562 to 7311 km) in the four-year period 1905–1908, there was a fairly constant rate of increase during the next 30 years, reaching a total of 11 144 miles (17 943 km) by the end of 1937.

In the 1880s the military became interested in the idea of switching to standard gauge to improve the railways' abilities to move vital war supplies, and a committee was formed to consider the matter. Nothing had happened by the end of the century, by which time the military were more concerned about the need to nationalise the system. After this had been carried out, others continued to press for wider track, and the 1911 budget included funds for gauge conversion, but the idea was opposed and aban-

A *Tsubame* ('Swallow') Limited-Express near the River Seta, between Kyoto and Maibara, on the old Tokaido Line in 1954, hauled by C62 4-6-4 No. 30.
Yasumi Kuroiwa

Part of the experimental layout near Yokohama to test the possibilities of changing the track gauge in about 1915. This is gauntleted, or interlaced, track rather than the mixed gauge arrangement using only three rails which may be used in the Seikan Tunnel in the Future.
Transportation Museum, Tokyo

doned. Five years later, however, some trials were actually carried out on a mixed-gauge test track near Yokohama, but in 1919 the idea was finally rejected. Some private railways, however, use standard gauge.

After the end of the Pacific War, the state-owned Japanese railway system became the Japanese National Railways (JNR) in 1949. Its total mileage in 1945 had been 12 462 (20 056 km), with the private railways contributing another 3444 miles (5543 km), and the nationalised system subsequently grew to over 20 000 km (12 427 miles) by 1954. The JNR network reached its greatest extent in 1981 when it stretched for 21 419 km (13 309 miles). As described in Chapter 7, this government organisation developed into an unwieldy monolith and was split in 1987 into a number of separate companies. Each now has a normal commercial structure, with the government initially holding all the shares, but, for the three large companies operating the Shinkansen network, the majority of the shares of each have now been sold on the stock market. Many local lines, in large conurbations as well as rural areas, remained in private ownership. Some of these were mineral railways, while the operations of others resembled those of North American 'Inter-Urbans'. A lot of these have closed during the last four decades, but Tokyo and many other large cities could not operate if it were not for the private and municipal railways, above and below ground, which supplement the former nationalised mainline companies.

CHAPTER 3

The First Japanese High-Speed Railway Project

As Japan's involvements in mainland Asia increased during the late 1930s, the need for better communications between the Kanto area around Tokyo and the far west of Japan became critical for the first time, as ports in that part of the country provided the easiest shipping links with China and Korea. To relieve the already-burdened Old Tokaido Line, a proposal was put forward for a totally new route between Tokyo and Osaka. It would be used by fast, new electric services, which were already being given the nickname 'Bullet Trains' - *dangan ressha* in Japanese.

The new, broad-gauge, route was also to be more direct, which would involve the construction of many more tunnels through the outlying hills and mountains which stretch towards the country's Pacific coast. There were even grandiose ideas for an undersea link with the Asian mainland, but these were probably more ahead of the then current technology than Mathieu-Favier's plans for a Channel Tunnel were at the time of Napoleon!

Tunnels are always on the critical path for any railway construction project, so, in the late 1930s, work on the new line commenced at the site of one of those needed for the first stretch of the 'New Trunk Line' or *Shinkansen*. A formal ground-breaking ceremony (*kikoshiki*) was held on a hill close to the hot-springs resort of Atami, some 60 miles (100 km) south-west of Tokyo, at what was to have been one of the portals of the Shin-Tanna Tunnel. In addition to the Shinto priests, Japanese Imperial Railways' officials and representatives of the government attended, with all the formality and dignity such an occasion demanded.

Actual construction work began immediately afterwards on the new railway, which was intended to link Tokyo and Osaka in the unheard of time of 4 hours, less than half that required by the existing line. Osaka was only to be the end of the first stage, and a 15-year programme would see the Shinkansen being extended all the way to the port of Shimonoseki, the most westerly city in Honshu. Three weeks after the standards for the new line had been adopted in 1941, the Pacific War started, which changed national priorities, and work on the new line slowed down as mate-

rials and funds were switched to more immediate military needs. Finally, as the country came under direct attack, the project was finally abandoned in June 1944, and the remaining engineers and their construction crews were switched to building air-raid shelters.

In the mid-1950s, as Japan's post-war economy began to prosper, the need for more capacity on the Old Tokaido Line again came to the fore, this time for commercial and industrial purposes rather than military ones. A study group was set up in 1956 to see how the route's capacity could be increased, and in May 1957 a vitally significant symposium was held at the Yamaha Hall in the Ginza district of Tokyo. It was organised by JNR's Railway Technical Research Institute, to consider the current developments taking place with high-speed railways elsewhere in the world.

During the discussions, proposals were made for a completely new line between Tokyo and Osaka, capable of taking 'Special Super Express' trains travelling at 250 km/h (155 m.p.h.), which would give journey times of just three hours. Nearly 40 years later, at the Tokaido Shinkansen 30-Year Commemorative Conference, held in Kyoto in 1994, Professor Satoru Sone of Kogakuin University, Tokyo, recalled how he had attended the symposium as a high-school teenager, and was so impressed by the presentations that he promptly decided to study electrical engineering when he went to university. The launch of few major transportation initiatives can be pin-pointed with such precision as the Shinkansen.

Correctly-speaking, the word *Shinkansen* means 'New Main Network', but the term very quickly came to be applied to the trains themselves, and that dual nomenclature is used throughout this book. It is somewhat ironic that the French high-speed lines are commonly referred to as 'TGVs', although that acronym actually stands for *Train à Grande Vitesse* (High-Speed Train), and few writers these days use the correct term *Ligne à Grande Vitesse* for the infrastructure. In the Japanese language nouns do not have separate singular and plural forms, so it is incorrect to refer to *Shinkansen*s, either for the trains or the routes.

CHAPTER 4

Birth of the Tokaido Shinkansen

As described in Chapter 2, by the 1950s the original Tokaido Line was the main passenger transport artery for an extremely important sector of Japan. Although its route length was only some 3% of the country's railway system, it was by then carrying 24% of all JNR's passenger traffic, and 23% of its freight. The rate of growth was also far higher for this line than any others in the country, and, in spite of having been electrified throughout in 1956, it had become impossible to introduce any more trains because track capacity was saturated. In 1957 the Ministry of Transport set up the Japanese National Railways Trunk Line Investigation Committee to look into the problem. It concluded that the traffic demand over this vital stretch was likely to double by 1975, even allowing for increased road and air competition. The construction of a completely new line was thus vital.

Various different options for constructing the new facility were considered by Hideo Shima, the Vice-President/ Engineering for JNR from 1955 until 1963. In February 2000, Tutomu Morimura, the Deputy Director General of JR-Central's Technical Research and Development Division, gave the Sir Seymour Biscoe Tritton Lecture to the Institution of Mechanical Engineers in London. He told his audience that Mr Shima's philosophy was to 'Carefully and systematically to build up technology that had been developed and proven in Japan and abroad'.

It was decided that the new line would only carry fast passenger trains, leaving the existing system for local passenger workings and freight services. Multiple-unit stock powered from a modern a.c. electrification system would permit the running of frequent high-speed trains on the new line. Three different possibilities were considered: additional Japanese-gauge tracks could be constructed either parallel to the existing ones or on a new alignment, or a completely new standard-gauge line could be built, comparable to those in Europe.

The first alternative was found to be impracticable for several reasons, in much the same way as BR quickly dismissed the idea of building the high-speed link from London to the Channel Tunnel alongside one of the existing routes. Curves on the old line, laid out for nineteenth-cen-tury speeds, were too sharp for the high speeds required. Large centres of population had also grown up beside the old tracks, which were plagued by more than 1000 level-crossings. The only exception finally made was with the alignment in central Tokyo, where the only available space was along the existing rail corridor. Here the two new standard-gauge lines were constructed between an elevated motorway and the six multiple-track 'Japanese-gauge' tracks through the Ginza area, and speeds on the Shinkansen are correspondingly restrained as the trains snake their way between the skyscrapers.

After the decision to construct a completely new line had been made, it followed that there were advantages in favour of using standard gauge (4 feet 8½ inches or 1435mm). This enabled them to adopt techniques which were not compatible with the older facilities, and 'released JNR from old habits'. Shinji Sogo, the JNR President from 1955 to 1963, took the proposals to the government and, having obtained their approval in 1958, construction commenced the following year.

It was estimated that construction costs would be just under ¥200 billion, and the work would occupy 5 years. As government changes could occur during this period, Mr. Sogo was advised to apply for a substantial loan from the World Bank, which would make it difficult for any subsequent governments to change the plans. In the light of earlier research by the Railway Technical Research Institute, the new line was designed for a maximum speed of 155 m.p.h. (250 km/h). That was, at the time, far in excess of commercial services being operated on any railway in the world, and such a speed had only been exceeded by the brief maxima reached during the French experimental runs south of Bordeaux in March 1955. Those had nearly ended in disaster, with the track buckling as BB9004 hurtled over it at 205.7 m.p.h. (331.0 km/h).

Mr Sogo realised that it would be unwise to confront the conservative banking community with proposals for 155mph trains. The scheme was accordingly presented with the maximum service speed fixed at 125mph (200km/h), and JNR was granted a loan of $80 million in May 1961 – a far

Map showing the route of the Tokaido Shinkansen.　　*JNR*

Table 4.1		
Major Tokaido Shinkansen Viaducts		
	Length	
	Metres	Yards
Enoo	786	840
Fuji River	1373	1502
Oi River	987	1079
Tenryu River	901	985
Kiso River	1001	1095
Source: JNR		

The ceremonial opening of the Tokaido Shinkansen at 06.00 on 1 October 1964. The tape is being cut by JNR's President Ishida, while Mr Kato, the Director of the Shinkansen Bureau, stands by to break-out the streamers from the decorated ball. *Collection of Akira Hoshi*

more significant sum of money in those days than it appears now. In practice, after the new line had been built, the service speed was jacked up slightly to 130 m.p.h. (210 km/h). To anticipate another chapter in the Shinkansen story, the loan was repaid in 1981, 16½ years after the Tokaido Line started operating commercially.

As has happened with nearly every major railway construction programme throughout the world, from George Stephenson's Stockton & Darlington Railway onwards, the cost of the Tokaido Shinkansen exceeded budget, even after the initial one had been revised, and the final total came to ¥380 billion. With the vital need to get it into service for the 1964 Tokyo Olympic Games, the completion was not delayed, and it opened on time. Nevertheless, because of the cost over-run, both the JNR President (Mr Sogo) and his Vice President/Engineering (Mr Shima) considered it their duty to resign, and neither of these individuals attended the opening ceremony. In due time, however, their contribution was publicly recognised. On the southern end of the Shinkansen platforms 18 and 19 at Tokyo Central station there is a monument to Mr Shinji Sogo, while among Mr Hideo Shima's international honours was the James Watt Gold Medal from the UK Institution of Mechanical Engineers.

The New Infrastructure

The New Tokaido Line was designed so that many of its 10 intermediate stations provided an easy interchange with those on the earlier line. Where the new station was on a different site from the locality's existing main-line station,

the prefix Shin- was used, as with Shin-Yokohama and Shin-Osaka. Between stations the shortest route was followed, with the maximum of straight sections, separated by curves with a minimum radius of 2.5 km (1½ miles). (This was only a marginal increase on those on BR's East Coast route where the figure is 2.3 km). As a result the rail distance by the Tokaido Shinkansen between Tokyo and the terminus at the new station of Shin-Osaka was 25 miles less than that by the old route, which, in itself, gives a significant time advantage. The down-side of this was that more expensive civil engineering work was needed, and some 13% of the line is in tunnel, with 33% on bridges or viaducts. While there are no particularly long tunnels, there are five lengthy viaducts, listed in order from Tokyo in Table 4.1

The whole line is securely fenced throughout, and protective mesh screens are erected on both sides of overbridges to prevent anything falling on to the tracks. Access to the line is normally forbidden while trains are running, so maintenance work has to take place during the six-hour shut-down of the system every night. When renewal of the track with heavier rails began in 1972, it was found to be impossible to complete the relaying of pointwork during this normal overnight gap, and on some eight mornings a year the system did not restart until noon. Between 1975 and 1982 such shut-downs took place on 44 occasions, but, with today's passenger loadings it is no longer possible to countenance such interruptions. This provides an example of how the operation of the whole system has been fine-tuned during three decades.

A 1960 view on the Old Tokaido Line, showing a Japanese-gauge *Kodama* Limited-Express near Ofuna. *Yasumi Kuroiwa*

The Tokaido Shinkansen consists basically of a straight-forward twin-track railway, with the up and down lines having their centres 4.2 metres (13¾ feet) apart. At the major stations of Shin-Osaka (which has now become a through one, as described in Chapter 5), Kyoto and Nagoya, where all Tokaido Shinkansen trains originally stopped and most still do, the platforms are situated on the running lines. Elsewhere, however, there are loops serving the platforms, so trains passing through on the central tracks at full speed are kept well clear of anyone waiting to join a slower service. There is thus no risk of them being swept off by the slip-stream of passing trains. Nevertheless raised and coloured surface markings are provided a short distance back from the edge of the platform which people have to keep behind as stopping trains run in or depart. (The writer was once whistled at by a railway policeman for overstepping one of these to take a photograph of an arriving train!)

Continuously-welded rails were used, fastened to concrete sleepers carried on ballast, except on viaducts. Turnouts were provided with moveable noses to make the ride smoother. Gradients as steep as 1 in 50 (2%) were adopted in places, but in the main they were limited to 1 in 67 (1.5%). A special testing train, nicknamed 'Doctor Yellow' from its colour, runs over the line every 10 days or so, and records the alignments of the track and the overhead wires. Information from its data-loggers is then used to pinpoint and subsequently order any maintenance required. Nowadays all of this is contracted out, and the work is only paid for when the next journey by the recording train confirms that it had been completed satisfactorily.

Although overhead wires providing a 1500 V d.c. supply had been used on many of the electrified Japanese narrow-gauge lines, such a low voltage could not transmit the high powers needed for the new trains. Japan's weather can exacerbate the problem, as, during the summer, a third of the railway's electricity consumption in the Tokyo area is needed for the trains' air-conditioning equipment. Accordingly a 25 kV a.c. system was adopted for the Shinkansen, which had been used successfully by the SNCF for their major electrification scheme between Thionville and Valenciennes in north-east France, completed in 1954. Fifteen months later the British Transport Commission announced it would use the same system for the lines being electrified under its Modernisation Plan. There were potential clearance problems for the higher-voltage overhead wires on the old UK routes, but this was overcome by adopting a twin-voltage system (6.25 kV as well as 25 kV), which created a number of operational problems that were not finally removed until the last of the 6.25 kV stretches disappeared in 1989.

With a completely new railway like the Shinkansen, it was possible to provide the necessary clearances for the high-voltage overhead wires from the beginning, but in Japan there was a frequency problem. In that country there are two separate electricity 'Grids', operating at different frequencies, which are separated by the line of the Fuji River, some 70 miles west of Tokyo. In the 1960s the technology available meant that the equipment for frequency conversion was too heavy to be accommodated on the trains, so was sited at the feeder stations on the ground. As three quarters of the New Tokaido Line are in the 60 Hz area, the trains were built to use current at this frequency throughout, and huge rotary converters were provided at the two feeder stations in 50 Hz territory east of the dividing line. The contact wire on the Shinkansen system was supported by a compound catenary.

Bogie of Series 0 Shinkansen.   *JR-Central*

It was decided, right at the outset, to do away with line-side signals, and provide the necessary indications for the driver inside the cab. In addition, they adopted what we now refer to as a comprehensive Automatic Train Protection system, although in Japanese parlance it is called **A**utomatic **T**rain **S**topper (ATS). If the speed exceeds that permitted, a warning bell sounds, and the rheostatic brake is automatically applied to reduce it. Signals are picked up from the coded track-circuits to indicate the maximum speed allowed at every point, and drivers control the power application and braking to conform to the indication shown. A fuller description is given later in this chapter.

Operations over the whole length of the New Tokaido Line are co-ordinated from the General Control Centre in Tokyo. Across the full length of one wall is a illuminated diagram of the whole track layout, with the position of every train shown by coloured lights and an identification number. In front of it are the desks of the local train controllers dealing with the movements on their own stretches of line. Behind them are other rows of desks accommodating supervisors, some dealing with the systems controlling the power supplies, signalling equipment, etc. As the Shinkansen was extended towards Hakata, the display was enlarged to include the additional lines, and a **Com**puter-Aided **Tra**ffic **C**ontrol system (COMTRAC) was installed when the extension to Okayama was opened in 1972.

The task of building a completely new high-speed line 320 miles long presented the civil engineers with immense technical and logistic problems. In spite of all the preliminary studies and design work, it was vital to try them out in practice. Accordingly a test section was built near Tokyo, on the alignment of the new line. Some of the early photographs showed the experimental rolling-stock on mixed-gauge track. This provided connections with the workshop, and was reminiscent of the mixed-gauge trials carried out in the Yokohama area as long ago as 1916. From August 1962, numerous trials took place along the 20-mile length of the test track proper, which involved different rolling-stock prototypes, as well as alternative signalling equipment and track structures.

In October that year a speed of 125 m.p.h. (200 km/h) was reached for the first time, and five months later a new record of 159 m.p.h. (256 km/h) was achieved. In Spring 1964 trial running of 6-car trains of production stock began between Kamonomiya and Atami, and then, in July, the first through train travelled from Tokyo to Osaka on the new line. A limited trial operation commenced on 25 August, in preparation for the ceremonial launch on 1 October.

The world's first high-speed railway was in operation, with trains running at 210 km/h (130 m.p.h.) wherever the brand-new formation had become stabilised.

The New Train Sets

In addition to designing and building an infrastructure to permit continuous high-speed running, JNR needed a completely new generation of trains. Although the Shinkansen represented a huge leap forward in railway technology and operating, the changes were evolutionary rather than revolutionary, and details of their design were based on existing, well-established practices.

An early decision was to arrange the electric traction in 'multiple-unit' form, as JNR referred to it, which gives the term a slightly different meaning from that understood in this country. Many Japanese EMU expresses, as well as the Shinkansen ones, do not combine and divide in the course of their daily rosters in the way some of the UK EMUs do. However the layout of their traction equipment resembles ours in that they comprise multiple similar installations.

As early as the 1950s JNR had developed the concept of using EMUs for middle-distance services, with their traction equipment spread along the length of the train, rather than concentrated in a locomotive at the head end. This gives a much lower maximum axle-load, as well as increasing the total adhesion weight available. That, in turn, enables higher accelerations to be used without wheel-spin,

Above: The original 'Doctor Yellow' multiple-inspection train. *JNR*

Right: A Series 0 Shinkansen heads away from the camera, showing the original construction of the overhead wiring. *JR-Central*

Left: A Series 0 Shinkansen emerges from a tunnel near Odawara. *Mikio Miura*

Below left: Monument on Platforms 18/19 at Tokyo station to Mr Shinji Sogo, the JNR President responsible for the realisation of the Shinkansen concept. *Mikio Miura*

Below: Plaque recording the starting-point of construction work on the Tokaido Shinkansen at Kamonomiya. *JR-Central*

Below right: Plaque at Tokyo Central station commemorating the inauguration of the Tokaido Shinkansen on 1 October 1964. *Mikio Miura*

and so can reduce journey times without the need for higher maximum speeds. In the 1960s, the idea of operating expresses with a locomotive at one end and a driving trailer at the other was not widely practised. Even if it had been practical for 16-car trains weighing upwards of 800 tonnes, the use of conventional locomotive haulage would have necessitated the terminal stations being far larger. This would have complicated their planning, especially in Tokyo.

The coach bodies were manufactured from steel, and were designed to be as light as possible, which resulted in maximum axle-loadings of only 16 tonnes - less than the SNCF adopted as standard for their TGVs a decade later. A pointed, streamlined shape was provided for the cars at the front and rear ends, and this quickly earned them their worldwide nickname of 'Bullet Trains'. A total of 8.9 MW (11 900 h.p.) was provided for traction purposes on the initial 12-car trains. To cope with the high speeds, a new design of bogie was adopted which eliminated hunting and also gave a satisfactory ride for passengers.

For many years after the Tokaido Line opened, the same stock was used for all trains, and further builds were needed to match the demand as traffic increased. The original stud of 360 cars (30 12-car sets) had become 2260 by the end of March 1982. By then some of the original cars were already on display in the Osaka and Tokyo Transport Museums, the front-end of one at the latter protruding dramatically from the front of the building! In due time it became uneconomic to maintain the earliest sets delivered, and they were replaced by more of the same general design. At that time they were just known as Shinkansen or 'Bullet Trains', and it was not until the completely different Series 100 trains were introduced on the Tokaido and Sanyo Lines in 1985 that it became customary to refer to the original design as 'Series 0' ('Series Zero').

An additional advantage of the multiple-unit system is that, with every axle powered, braking at speeds of over 30 m.p.h. could normally be carried out using a powerful electric rheostatic system, thus reducing the wear on the specially-designed disc brakes. Vehicles were constructed to operate as pairs, which simplified design, and subsequently enabled trains to be lengthened from the original 12 cars to the 16 needed today without altering their performance characteristics.

On the Series 0 trains, every axle was driven by its own 250 h.p. (185 kW) d.c. traction motor. Each of these was thus no more powerful than those fitted to one of BR's 4-Ceps (later Class 411) built in 1956. The Southern Region was well known to have been conservative in the design of its traction motors, and a decade later there were probably many more powerful ones installed in ordinary Japanese trains. The choice of such comparatively small motors provides a good example of how the Japanese avoided introducing revolutionary equipment, with its potential development problems, into their new high-speed trains.

One of the 16-car trains of the original design nevertheless had a total installed power of just under 15 900 h.p. (11.84 MW). This is comparable with the 16 400 h.p. (12.2 MW) available from a Eurostar for traction purposes under the 25 kV overhead wires. To meet the safety requirements for the Channel Tunnel, one of these European trains has only 12 traction motors, so each has an output of more than a megawatt. Such equipment was at the limit of contemporary technology, but the Japanese designers had achieved a similarly-powered train a quarter of a century earlier using existing equipment. Each pair of Shinkansen cars shared a single traction system. Every other coach carried a pantograph, while the electric traction equipment, such as the transformers and rectifiers, as well as the control gear, was distributed between the underfloor spaces on both cars. Their power control system used tap-changers on the secondary side of the transformers, comparable to the technology used on the UK Class 86s for the West Coast route.

Being designed for a completely new railway it was possible to optimise the vehicles' dimensions. Table 4.2 gives the comparative figures for the Shinkansen and standard Japanese stock, together with those for the British Rail Mk IVs used on the East Coast route, to provide a UK yardstick.

The actual bodies of the new coaches were some 20% greater in length than the previous Japanese standard. This added another 13 feet, which makes them 4½ feet longer than our Mk IV InterCity vehicles. Over their couplings these Shinkansen coaches were 25 metres long, so a 16-car train stretched for 400 metres, which is fractionally longer than one of the 2 +18 Eurostars. An ordinary Japanese coach is some 9 inches wider than the maximum that can be accommodated in this country, but the Shinkansen ones are wider still, giving the interior designers an extra 1.4 metres (4½ feet) to play with. We will see later how the resulting space has been utilised.

Table 4.2						
Dimensions of Shinkansen (Series 0) and Other Coaches						
	Length		Width		Height	
	Metres	Feet	Metres	Feet	Metres	Feet
Shinkansen*	24.5	80.4	3.38	11.1	3.98	13.1
JNR narrow-gauge	20.5	67.3	2.95	9.7	4.05	13.3
BR MkIV	23.0	75.5	2.73	9.0	4.00	13.0

* The front and rear cars are slightly longer than the intermediate ones.

Source: JNR

As trains rush in and out of tunnels at speeds of more than two miles per minute, pressure pulses are generated which can have unfortunate effects. In a reminiscent article published in the *JR Tokai Technical Report* at the time of the line's 30th Anniversary, Hideo Shima, who had been responsible for its engineering, commented that they had not foreseen two major problems that resulted from this. One was the pain caused to passengers' ears, and the other was the strong air currents blowing up through the toilets. So, as well as being equipped with a full air-conditioning system needed to deal with Japan's hot and humid summer weather, the Shinkansen cars had to be pressure-sealed. Special construction techniques are required for this, and it is the eventual deterioration of the seals which is usually the cause of a vehicle's withdrawal.

Taking advantage of the additional width of the body-shell, an ordinary Shinkansen coach has its seats in a 2 + 3 arrangement, compared with the normal 2 + 2 set-up used in Japan. The Shinkansen Green Cars, which are the equivalent of the UK First Class, have 2 +2 seating, whereas we can only manage a 2 + 1 arrangement. (It is worth mentioning that the average Japanese is less heavily-built than many of the European businessmen who travel first class!) Depending on the interior layout, ordinary Shinkansen coaches had up to 110 seats while a Green Car accommodated a maximum of 68. One of the original 16-car trains could seat 1208 ordinary passengers plus 132 in the Green Cars.

Many Japanese passengers prefer to face the direction of travel, so what in the UK is referred to as 'airline' style seating is provided in most trains, the Shinkansen included. As with the airborne variety, small fold-out or fold-down tables are provided, together with footrests in some instances. Originally each block of seats was fitted with 'swing-over' backs, so they could be switched to face the direction of travel whenever the train reversed. Various minor modifications were made, but later it was decided to provide a two-stage reclining facility, which required a change in the seat-back design. The three-seat blocks were fixed, but the two-seat ones were made to rotate, being released by a foot pedal. Staff in the terminus normally reverse them during the turn-round time, but the operation is an easy one, so groups of passengers wishing to hold a conversation can do this themselves, as long as it does not inconvenience other passengers. A similar facility was available in some of the DB first-class open coaches used on their Inter-City trains in the 1980s. In the later Series 100 trains, by eliminating a few of the seat rows, and spacing the others further apart, the three-seat blocks can also be rotated.

Small rooms for handicapped passengers are provided in certain cars, and space was made for wheelchairs in some of the open saloons by removing a few of the aisle seats. Access to the Shinkansen is easy as the heights of JR platforms are comparable to those used in the UK, rather than the lower ones used on most railways on mainland Europe. Originally the Shinkansen's doors were rather narrow, and those used for wheelchair access had to be widened.

Triple-glazed windows are used, with the two inner layers separated by an air space to cut down heat and noise transmission. Originally quite large windows were provided, each of them covering a pair of seat rows, which made those in the Green Cars just over 6 feet wide. It proved difficult to change this type of glazing if there was any damage, and smaller windows became the norm, one per row of seats. Again those paying more to travel in the Green Cars benefited from windows which were a quarter as large again as the ordinary ones. All seats line up with the windows, and there are none with restricted vision like there are on the UK Mk III standard-class coaches, let alone the complete blank walls that face some passengers in the TGVs and their variants.

The standard body-shell was used to provide a variety of different interior layouts. Various facilities were provided at the coach-ends, with Japanese and 'Western' toilets being available. The equipment not only used 'retention' tanks, rather than discharging the waste on to the tracks, but equipment was provided to recycle some of the water, after deodorising and disinfecting it. Certain coaches had a chilled-water drinking-fountain, while others were provided with a pay-phone in the vestibule area. Sliding exterior doors were used, and an audible warning was given of their pending closure by the platform loudspeaker.

Catering arrangements on the original units have changed considerably over the years. Originally buffet areas were provided in two separate coaches, and these were supplemented by a number of different trolley services up and down the train. A feature was the provision of a speed-ometer in each buffet area so passengers could check how fast the train was travelling. In 1974 a proper dining car was introduced, and advantage was taken of the vehicles' greater width to provide a side corridor, which separated the diners from those walking up and down the train. This longitudinal partition was glazed, 'to enable dining passengers to see Mount Fuji', as the advertising had it. As this view was, at best, only available for a very short time on each journey, one suspects that it was the general ambience which was really the important factor. About a third of the vehicle's length was used for food preparation, and the seating area had tables for two and four on opposite sides of the centre aisle. Nothing changes quite so fast as eating habits, and, eventually the demand for set meals decreased on the original units, and the waitress-served facility was withdrawn, the dining-cars on all Tokaido Shinkansen being withdrawn as uneconomic in March 2000.

At the 30th Anniversary High-Speed Railway Conference at Kyoto in 1994, the writer chaired an international *Zadankai* - an informal discussion group – one of the subjects being on-train catering. It was a senior SNCF manager who commented that the popular Japanese 'Bento Lunch Box', containing rice, meat, fish, pickled vegetables and a pair of chop-sticks, provided by far the most flexible feeding arrangement in the world for railway use, with rival caterers able to provide their own versions at the stations or on the trains. The disappearance of the dining cars on the Shinkansen sets must be viewed against this background.

The front and rear cars differed considerably from the rest of those in a Shinkansen set, as they have to provide facilities for the drivers, as well as the equipment needed to control the train. The cabs, with their V-shaped windscreens, were mounted high in the body, and the seats for

the two crew were fixed to a raised 'half-deck' across the front, which was reached using an intermediate step. A central flap between the two seats could be raised if access was needed to the equipment compartment in the nose, but in its 'down' position was strong enough to support a folding chair for my wife when we travelled in the cab from Fukuyama and Hiroshima in 1982, so she could watch the track ahead. The author stood on the left-hand step behind the driver to observe how the control systems operated, and there was plenty of room for the traction inspector, as well as for Mr Niinobe, the JNR officer acting as our guide, to stand behind us in the roomy cab. The ATC equipment is housed in cabinets across the rear bulkhead.

On either side of the 'Bullet Nose', which can be removed to expose the swing-down emergency coupling, the blue side-skirting sweeps down to rail-level to form a 'cow-catcher', with strakes on it to smooth the airflow. It is clearly a fairly-substantial chunk of metal, but the real protection consists of a semi-circular sandwich, fabricated from several separate thicknesses of high-strength steel plate, hidden behind it.

Automatic Train Control and Other Safety Systems

In the 1960s, the idea of controlling the trains without the use of lineside signals was unprecedented on any main-line railway, let alone one where the speeds were to be higher than any other in the world. This was nevertheless achieved on the pioneering Tokaido Shinkansen by transmitting coded signals to the trains via track circuits, and each driving-car has a receiving coil mounted just in front of its leading axle. The latter completes the track-circuit, and the coil picked up the code, which was filtered and fed to logic circuits. With the aid of an accurate speedometer, the driver could then be supplied with a display showing the maximum speed permitted at all times, and the equipment applied the brakes if it was exceeded.

Open track is divided into sections, each 3000 metres (3300 yards) long, which corresponded to those used with conventional block signalling. Track circuits identify the location of every train on the system, and only when the block section ahead is clear is a train permitted to move forward. Should it attempt to pass into an occupied section at low speed, the track-circuit code will cause it to stop immediately. Under the original speed regime, if the train ahead was only one block away, the maximum speed allowed was no more than 30 km/h (19 m.p.h.), but the figure went up to 160 km/h (100 m.p.h.), and then the full 210 km/h

(131 m.p.h.) if there were two or three clear blocks between the trains. A Shinkansen train could thus only run at full speed if there were more than two clear block sections between it and the train in front. This gap of 6 km (3¾ miles) was more than sufficient to enable it to brake from full speed to a standstill clear of the preceding train, for which just over 2 km (1¼ miles) was actually required.

On the Series 0 trains, the speedometer in front of the driver had a horizontal red bar as an indicator. The scale was divided into sections, and, as the end of the bar moved from one into the next, each in turn was illuminated from behind. Above the scale figures for 30, 70, 110, 160, and 210 (km/h) were five circular windows, one of which was lit to indicate the current maximum authorised speed in kilometres per hour. (These correspond to 19, 43, 68, 100 and 130 m.p.h.). As long as the speed was below the maximum permitted, the driver could utilise whatever setting of his ten-notch power lever he wanted, but if the speed exceeded the limit, there was an audible warning, power was cut, and the brakes automatically applied.

On the occasion of my journey, the driver showed me how this worked, by letting speed creep up above the 210-km/h mark. As the next section of the speedometer became illuminated, a bell rang, and the resulting quick dab of the rheostatic brakes smartly reduced our speed to 190. There is no cruise-control system like that used on the BR Class 91s and 90s, and drivers take pride in juggling with the controller as the gradients change to maintain the speed the schedule requires.

It will be seen that there were indications for more speed bands than those mentioned earlier, which were the ones that applied in the 1970s on open track. Additional restrictions were needed to ensure the train slowed appropriately over certain curves, or as it took the turnouts into station platforms. Most of the speed reduction for a station stop is carried out automatically, but, having entered the platform, the driver presses a white button, which enables him to take over control. He can then briefly reapply power before using the air brake to bring the train to a stand exactly in line with the marker. At all Japanese stations, very precise stops are needed because passengers queue behind the marks on the platform that indicate exactly where the doors will be. Should the driver fail to stop, the change of track-circuit at the exit end of the platform loop would immediately bring the train to a halt. To the observer in the cab this process appears to take quite a long time, but, on

the later Tohoku Shinkansen, stopping at a station added just over three minutes to a train's schedule compared with passing through non-stop. Slowing cost 100 seconds and acceleration to line-speed a further 90.

To ensure reliability the ATC signal processing units were triplicated, and, if the output from one of them differed from those from the other two, it was ignored. In principle this whole system has many of the features of the 'Transmission-Based' one which the European Union is currently seeking to get introduced, 30 years later, to enable trains to run unhindered across national boundaries in continental Europe. While the Shinkansen's engineers did have the advantage of starting with a clean sheet of paper, and had only one railway administration to satisfy, they were well ahead of world thinking at the time their system was put into service.

When the Shinkansen was extended from Shin-Osaka to Okayama in 1972, the ATC was linked up to a new **Com**puter-Aided **Tra**ffic **C**ontrol system (COMTRAC), the operation of which is shown diagramatically in Figure 4.1. It is designed to control the routing of trains, plotting the scheduled running diagrams, and managing the utilisation of train-crews and rolling-stock. It consists of three main computers:

PRC (**P**rogrammed **R**oute **C**ontrol) sets the route for each train from its diagram number as it approaches a station, MAP (**M**an-machine **A**dvanced **P**rocesssor) produces the displays showing the position of trains, and the track occupation, etc at stations, including any abnormal conditions, EDP (**E**lectronic **D**ata **P**rocessing Computer) draws up the daily operating plan for rolling-stock and train-crews, and can provide a new running diagram if there is any upset to the scheduled timetable. It also collects failure data, which it transmits to SMIS (**S**hinkansen **M**anagment **I**nformation **S**ystem), a vital function in the quest for ever better reliability.

Tokyo Control is connected to every station along the line by optical-fibre links, which are constantly passing information in both directions. Each station has a local interlocking installation to operate its points, and, if everything is running to schedule, the necessary instructions are automatically sent to turn them in the correct direction. Only in unusual circumstances would the local controller take over this function, using his own terminal to initiate the operation. The interlocking works in harmony with the ATC system to ensure that the appropriate speed restrictions are transmitted by the track circuits to every approaching train.

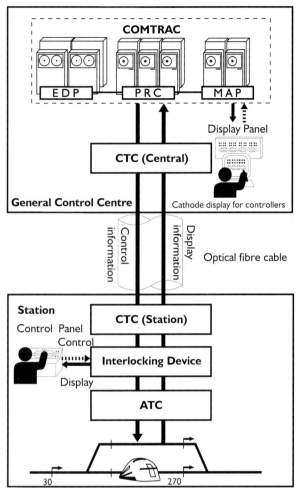

Figure 4.1. A diagram of the COMTRAC control system, as introduced in 1972 at the time of the opening of the first stretch of the Sanyo Shinkansen

A special radio system permits direct communication between the Control Centre and each train, but what looked like an 'aerial' on the roof of each cab was actually a voltage-detector for the catenary. In cases of emergency the driver of a train can also actuate the track beacons so they give stop signals, and it is also possible, from the train, to cut off power from the overhead wires for its section.

Japan lies in an earthquake zone, and twice this century there have been devastating major shocks. To guard against any affecting the Shinkansen, seismometers were installed at electrical feeder stations to cut the power if an earthquake was detected. During the writer's journey on the Tohoku Shinkansen in 1982 our train suddenly ground to a halt as it was approaching the then terminus at Omiya. The emergency lights replaced the bright fluorescent overhead lighting, while the hum of the under-floor equipment lapsed into silence. In addition to the sensors sited in the feeder stations there were some on the Pacific coast, and one of them had triggered the shut-down. A suitable announcement was made while we stood for 10 minutes, after which the lights came on again and we were able to complete the final few miles of our journey.

These original detectors could only measure the main (secondary) shock-waves, and the information from three or more of these had to be processed to locate the earthquake's epicentre and severity. In 1992 a new type of detector was installed - UrEDAS (**Ur**gent **E**arthquake **D**etection and **A**larm **S**ystem). Any one of these is able, by itself, to carry out the necessary calculations from the arrival of

the faster primary wave, and so shut down the system that much quicker. There are 14 of these new detector stations covering the Tokaido Shinkansen area.

When the Great Hanshin Earthquake struck Kobe early in the morning of 17 January 1995, the Shinkansen system had not yet begun its operations for the day, so UrEDAS was not tested in anger, although its data-loggers would undoubtedly have been examined to see how the system performed. Considerable damage was done to parts of the Sanyo Shinkansen in the area, the worst being the collapse of a few viaducts supported by reinforced concrete piers. Following instructions from the Ministry of Transport, urgent measures were taken to reinforce vulnerable railway structures throughout the country. The different systems of civil engineering used on the various Shinkansen clearly affected the scope of the strengthening needed. However, less than 12 months after the earthquake, West Japan Railway had begun work on more than 15 000 concrete viaduct columns, which are a feature of the civil engineering on the Sanyo Shinkansen. Steel 'corsets' were fitted round them and the annular gap filled with a special mortar. Steps were also taken to secure the girder spans to prevent them being moved off their supports laterally or longitudinally.

The Japanese islands also suffer from extremes of weather, particularly with typhoons. On two occasions one has rolled in within 48 hours of the writer's arrival in the country, and, even in a major city, the results were alarming. It is not only the exceptionally high winds which can do tremendous damage, but the torrential rain that accompanies them can cause widespread flooding as well as landslides. On the first occasion the resulting spate on the Fuji River took out the bridge on the Old Tokaido Line, and, as a precaution, a speed restriction was imposed on the corresponding 1,500-yard one on the Shinkansen. At various critical locations, therefore, wind-speed measurements are made continuously at some 50 points, and rain gauges are provided as well. If the wind reaches more than 25 m/s (56 m.p.h.) a speed restriction is applied. Should the wind speed exceed 30 m/s (67 m.p.h.), or the rainfall precipitation rate rise above a specified limit, the Shinkansen shuts down. From the public's point of view, plenty of warning of pending disruptions is available from other sources, such as radio and television bulletins.

The later Tohoku and Joetsu Shinkansen were built through very mountainous and snowy areas in the northern part of Honshu, and, as described later, the train-sets had to be designed specially to deal with quite heavy snow-falls. It again came as a surprise to the engineers that the Tokaido Shinkansen, in spite of being on roughly the same latitude as Gibraltar, also suffered from snow. Some of it is clearly of the 'wrong sort', so beloved by the UK press, as it is blown about by passing trains and some adheres to their undersides. When a warmer stretch of line is reached, it falls off in large lumps and flies all over the place, scattering the ballast which can damage the underfloor equipment. Lineside water sprays have accordingly been provided since 1967 at critical locations to damp down any such precipitation and prevent it flying about as a train passes. At the portals of some tunnels it has also been necessary to build shelters to prevent snowfalls blocking the track.

Train Services

Japanese railways have operated even-interval services for a long time, and on the busier routes the timetable comprises a sophisticated matrix of stopping trains and expresses of various sorts enabling passengers to minimise journey times by changing from one to the other en *route*.

On the main lines there is a long-standing tradition of naming the fastest trains, but the way it is done is very different from the UK. In many instances we only name the principal – and that usually also means the fastest – train in each direction. Japanese practice is to give every express, in both directions, a family name, and differentiate between them by adding numbers. As in North America, odd numbers are used for down trains, usually those from the Tokyo direction, and even numbers for those in the other. The names chosen are usually not as prosaic as ours, a good example being those that link Sapporo and Asahikawa in Hokkaido. The first morning train from Sapporo is *Lilac 1*, named after the well-known flowering shrub which grows extensively in the area. In the opposite direction the first train is *Lilac 2*, and the final one at night *Lilac 30*.

When the train services on the Tokaido Shinkansen were being planned in 1964 it was decided to operate two sorts of Super Express. Some would call at all 10 intermediate stations between Tokyo and Shin-Osaka (the new station built there for the Shinkansen), while most of those with the fastest overall timings would only stop intermediately at the major cities of Nagoya and Kyoto. In July that year the announcement was made that these trains would be known respectively as *Kodama* and *Hikari*, their English translations being 'Echo', and 'Light'. As light travels faster than sound, so a *Hikari* train is perceived as being faster than a *Kodama* one. Both names were already in use for trains elsewhere in Japan.

The original basic train service pattern comprised one of each sort of express in each direction every hour, but the daily total actually involved the operation of 60 trains: 28 *Hikari* and 32 *Kodama*. For most of the time one of each type of train ran every hour, the shorthand for which was 1H-1K. For good operational reasons it is never possible to estimate the actual number of trains running in a day from the basic *Hikari/Kodama* split alone. After November 1965, when the new track had bedded in, the service frequency was doubled, and the standard time for a *Hikari* between Tokyo and Osaka was cut to 3 hr 10 min, but the *Kodama* took a full four hours, so the 'non-stops' overtook the 'stoppers' while they made a call at one of the intermediate stations. This general system has continued ever since, but the details have changed as the number of trains operated has increased to the present average of 285 per day. This is the total of regularly-scheduled trains, including seasonal ones, but, over and above these, many extras are operated at holiday times, etc. (The very useful JR English-language timetable for the whole of the country only lists trains that run *every weekday* throughout the year, so its Shinkansen total is lower than that quoted).

For the first time in the world, trains were being regularly scheduled with start-to-stop averages of more than 100 m.p.h. (160 km/h), and, because of the standardised timetable and train formations, these were repeated not only every hour, but in due course this became several times per hour. As time progressed it was not only the *Hikari*

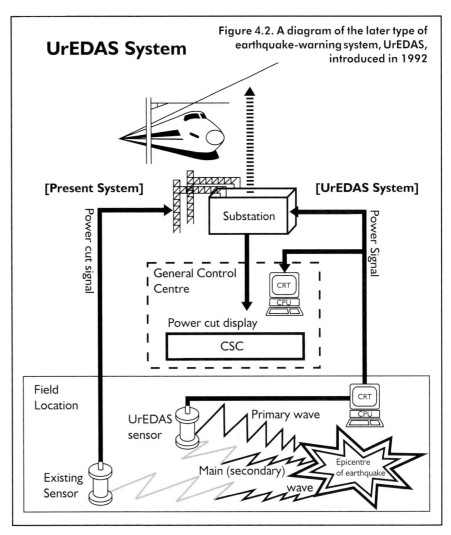

UrEDAS System

Figure 4.2. A diagram of the later type of earthquake-warning system, UrEDAS, introduced in 1992

which achieved fast averages, as some of the *Kodama* were required to do so too. As passenger demands squeezed more and more trains into the timetables, the *Kodama* had to get their skates on, in spite of their shorter start-to-stop runs, so they could clear the line for the next *Hikari*.

In 1975 *Railway Gazette International* began publishing a two-yearly survey of the fastest railway speeds in the world. That year there were 374 instances of Shinkansen trains with start-to-stop averages of more than 160 km/h (100 m.p.h.) every day, some of them running on the Sanyo Shinkansen which had opened by that time, as will be described in the next chapter. That year there was **one** solitary competitor in the world achieving an average of over 100 m.p.h. This was the SNCF's locomotive-hauled express *Etendard*, which averaged 101.7 m.p.h. (163.7 km/h) from St. Pierre des Corps to Poitiers. In the UK our fastest contemporary average was achieved by the one West Coast train which took 43½ minutes between Rugby and Watford, giving it an average of only 89.9 m.p.h. (144.6 km/h).

The fastest Shinkansen were the 104 different *Hikari* which took 121 minutes to cover the 212.5 miles (342.0 km) in either direction between Tokyo and Nagoya, giving them an average speed of 105.4 m.p.h. (169.6 km/h). All but four of them went on to average 104.3 m.p.h. (167.9 km/h) over the much shorter distance (83.4 miles – 134.3 km) between Kyoto and Nagoya. The operational advantages of having a single type of stock were demonstrated by the fact that 61 *Kodama* were scheduled to take the same running time between the stops at Maibara and Kyoto as the three *Hikari* which also called at the former. The distance between the two stations is only 43.3 miles (68.1 km), but the scheduled average was 101.6 mph (163.5 km/h).

Left: A Series 0 Shinkansen threads its way out of Tokyo alongside the Japanese-gauge tracks near Shimbashi. *Mikio Miura*

As shown in Table 4.3, the passenger numbers and passenger-kilometres boomed during the Tokaido Line's first eight years of operation. JNR's accounting periods closely correspond to the UK's income tax years, and run from 1 April to 31 March. The Tokaido Shinkansen was the only Japanese high-speed line in existence until 1972, when the first section of the Sanyo Shinkansen, from Shin-Osaka to Okayama, started operations on 15 March. From then on through trains operated between the two lines, so it is not easy to make comparisons between the figures for before and after this date. We will examine later the effect of this and the Hakata extension on the total level of passenger business.

The first full year's figures were almost treble those for the initial half-year, and the number of passengers continued to increase steadily, doubling again by 1969. There was a big boost in 1970 due to EXPO' 70, which was held that year at Osaka, when more than a third of its visitors used the Shinkansen to reach that city. The passenger-kilometres followed much the same pattern, as overall the fairly steady fall-off in the average distance each of them travelled was quite small – from 221 to 191 miles (355 to 308 km) over the whole period, although EXPO' 70 produced a short-term blip to 205 miles (330 km).

In order to handle all this extra business, more trains had to be run and additional stock obtained. Table 4.4 shows how the average daily numbers of trains changed, and lists the total number of Shinkansen cars in service. The increases in train numbers and coaches owned by JNR, as shown in table 4.4, can be compared with the rise in passengers given in Table 4.3. It will be seen that although annual passenger numbers increased by no less than 175% over the 1965–1972 period, the number of trains run during the day had only doubled, in spite of the 3H–6K service pattern, although coaching-stock numbers were up by 143%. Clearly much more efficient use was being made of the stock, and trains were fuller.

Table 4.5 shows the Tokaido Line's financial performance for its first seven and a half years of operation. It may be difficult to relate to such large amounts of a foreign currency a quarter of a century ago, but the rapidity at which the line became profitable can easily be appreciated. During this period total profits amounted to no less than ¥383 billion, which needs to be equated with the cost of building the line. That had finally reached ¥380

billion compared with the original budget of just under ¥200 billion. The enhanced capital had thus been recovered in seven years from the line going into service, a remarkable achievement.

It is also worth noting that the financial year 1964/65 marked the point where JNR's revenue, as a whole, fell below its expenses, and two years later it was having to carry forward a steadily rising total of exceptional debts. In spite of the increasing profitability of the Tokaido Shinkansen, twenty years later these debts had reached more than ¥10 trillion.

Ticketing and Seat Reservation

The fare structure on Japanese railways is comparatively complex. Fundamentally the cost of a ticket is based on the distance travelled, but this basic fare is only valid on stopping trains. On the ordinary lines there are supplements for 'Express' and 'Limited-Express' trains, which again are distance-related. As with the French TGVs, the tariff distances on the Shinkansen routes are based on the original mileages, on top of which everyone using the Bullet Trains pays a 'Super-Express' supplement. Since the introduction of the faster *Nozomi* services, referred to in Chapter 8, they attract a higher one still.

As mentioned earlier, Shinkansen trains have two classes of accommodation. The ordinary coaches provide 3+2 seating, while in the 'Green Cars', the Japanese name for First Class, they are arranged in a 2+2 formation. Whole coaches are allocated for ordinary 'Reserved-Seat' and 'Unreserved-Seat' passengers. On a British train someone travelling without having booked a seat in advance can utilise an unoccupied one as long as it has not been reserved by someone else. With the Shinkansen different arrangements apply, as the supplements for travel in the two

Table 4.3
Tokaido Shinkansen Passengers 1964–1972

Year	Passenger Journeys (million)	Passenger-kilometres (billion)
1964/65*	11.0	3.9
1965/66	31.0	10.7
1966/67	43.8	14.5
1967/68	55.2	18.0
1968/69	65.9	21.0
1969/70	71.6	22.8
1970/71	84.6	27.9
1971/72	85.4	26.8

* Line only open for half of year.

Source: JNR

Table 4.4
Tokaido Shinkansen
Numbers of Trains Operated and Coaches in Service
1964–1972

Year	Hikari	Kodama	Total	Coaches Owned
	Numbers of Trains per Day			
1964/65*	28	32	60	360
1965/66	52	58	110	480
1966/67	56	65	121	600
1967/68	60	78	138	684
1968/69	66	104	170	792
1969/70†	76	124	200	1044
1970/71	78	135	213	1140
1971/72	92	127	219	1164

* Line only open for half of year.

† Including interest and depreciation.

Source: JNR

Table 4.5
Tokaido Shinkansen Revenue and Expenses 1964–1972
(Billions of Yen)

Year	Revenue	Expenses†	Profit/Loss
1964/65*	19	27	-8
1965/66	55	68	-13
1966/67	89	73	16
1967/68	110	75	35
1968/69	127	78	49
1969/70	165	86	79
1970/71	209	91	117
1971/72	199	91	108

* Line only open for half of year.

† Including interest and depreciation.

Source: JNR

types of car vary. While passengers are encouraged to book seats before travelling, it is possible to take an unoccupied seat in a 'Reserved' coach and pay the fee to the conductor. However it is not easy to find out which seats are free, because seat-reservation labels are not used, as with the French TGVs and Eurostars, but reservations are compulsory on these European trains. A reservation system that does not use labels on the seats does, however, have an important advantage – it is possible for reservations to be made right up to the last minute before the joining passenger's train arrives in the station.

Train formations have varied depending on whether the set is used on a *Hikari* or a *Kodama* service, while numerous other changes have taken place during the last 30 years to match operational and passenger requirements. After privatisation, with over-crowding on certain of the fast Tokaido Shinkansen trains, more spacious 2+2 seating was provided in the 'Reserved-Seat' ordinary cars of the Series 0 sets working the *Kodama*, to entice more passengers into them.

To give readers an idea of the fares and supplements, Table 10.9 in Chapter 10 lists the costs of different classes of single-journey tickets for the 320-mile journey between Tokyo and Shin-Osaka as they were in 1999/2000.

The construction of a completely new, stand-alone, high-speed railway required the provision of a number of specialised commercial systems, amongst them one to handle ticketing and seat-booking. JNR had already developed MARS (**Ma**gnetic electronic or **M**ulti-**A**ccess **R**eservation **S**ystem) for limited-express trains, and a special system, MARS101, was introduced six months before the Shinkansen began commercial operation. Although it could handle only 30 000 seats at any given time, it was also used for the new high-speed line. The central computer was located at Kunitachi, a suburb of Tokyo, and station booking offices had links with it. Subsequently, as Shinkansen traffic built up, the system has been up-graded several times to cope with the demand.

Various different designs of ticket-issuing machine have been tried at Shinkansen stations. When the high-speed line was extended to Hakata in early 1975, a system was introduced which enabled seat reservations to be made by keying in the necessary information on a push-button telephone. The passenger still has to call at the booking office to pay for and pick up the ticket after arriving at the station. Many travellers find this more bother than it is worth, so a new system was tried with comprehensive terminals at the entrance to stations which could accept banknotes or a credit card, and issue the ticket, like machines on the SNCF's TGV lines, and, more recently, on some British stations. Operators in stations and other places currently issuing tickets and reservations used a 'touch-screen' system to communicate with the central computer.

Like all such systems the world over, this type of equipment has a limited life, being overtaken by altered passenger requirements or changes in technology. On the Shinkansen in particular, the steadily-rising number of travellers provides a constant challenge.

Originally no part of a Shinkansen train was officially a 'Non-Smoking' area, but, with changing public attitudes, in 1980, for the first time, Car No.1 (the vehicle at the Hakata end of the train) was so designated, and, as in other countries, the number of vehicles in which smoking is banned has since increased considerably.

CHAPTER 5
The Sanyo Extension

As we have seen, the Tokaido Shinkansen was an instant success, getting into profit in its third financial year of operations, as well providing a vital new means of transport between the Japanese capital and Osaka, the country's second largest commercial centre. The new 320-mile high-speed railway did not, however, reach the historic port of Kobe, the western end of the original Tokaido trunk line, let alone serve the remaining 300-mile stretch of Honshu that lies along the northern shore of the Inland Sea, where traffic over the 'Japanese-gauge' Sanyo line had also reached saturation. There was thus a good case to extend the high-speed line westwards from Osaka, and construction of what was to be known as the Sanyo Shinkansen was authorised by the Minister of Transport in September 1965. Construction work began in the following March, and four months later the Tokaido Shinkansen chalked up its 100 millionth passenger.

For financial reasons, the first Shinkansen extension was from Shin-Osaka station as far as Okayama, a distance of exactly 100 miles (160.9 km). Compared with the terrain traversed by the Tokaido Shinkansen, the new line had to cope with many more natural obstacles, and 58% of the route was built on viaducts or bridges, and no less than 35% in tunnel. The longest of the latter was the 16.25 km (10.1 mile) Rokko Tunnel in the initial stretch between Osaka and Kobe. The new Shin-Kobe station lies just outside the western end of this, and the line almost immediately dives into another tunnel. So cramped is that city for land that it has for years been reclaiming the sea-shore to provide sites for new port and manufacturing facilities.

The previous chapter referred to the initial problems Shinkansen passengers experienced as they shot in and out of tunnels, but those living alongside the line also suffered from noise and vibration. Open steel trusses were used for the viaducts and bridges on the Tokaido Shinkansen, and they radiated considerable noise as trains crossed them at over two miles per minute. For future construction it was accordingly decided to use reinforced concrete structures, with shorter spans supported on a closer series of piers. Tunnels could also cause lineside problems, as the pressure waves created as trains entered them were liable to produce unheralded loud noises at the other end.

In the light of the satisfactory experience with the operation of the Tokaido Shinkansen, the decision was taken to build the New Sanyo Line for a maximum speed of 260 km/h (162 m.p.h.), which necessitated easing the sharpest curves to a radius of 4 km instead of 2.5 km (2½ miles compared with 1½). The distance between the up and down tracks was widened, the centre-to-centre measurement being increased by 100 mm (4 in) to 4.3 metres. All these changes involved moving more earth for cuttings and tunnels, with consequent increase in first cost. Another additional expense was the use of nearly 16 km (10 miles) of slab track, but this had the advantage it would reduce the cost of future maintenance, although it did not help with the vibration problems.

As well as Shin-Kobe, there were three other stations on the new line, which came into service in March 1972. The total number of Shinkansen passengers immediately shot up by just over a quarter, and rose a further 17% the following year. Table 5.1 gives the details. The average daily numbers of trains operated over the combined Shinkansen also increased, with a basic 4H-4K service pattern being adopted initially. Although this was an apparent reduction on the 3H-6K one operated the previous year to cope with the crowds bound for EXPO '70 in Osaka, the total number of daily services actually increased. As mentioned in Chapter 4, the *Hikari/Kodama* split does not operate throughout the whole of the day, and the daily total of each type of train does not depend entirely on the basic pattern. The March 1972 changes were designed to meet passengers' requirements, particularly with the better connections provided with ordinary trains at Okayama. The overall details are given in Table 5.2, which includes information on the number of coaches in service.

Well before the new line between Osaka and Kobe was opened in March 1972, authorisation had been given for the second extension to Hakata on the island of Kyushu. This was

---

Table 5.1
Tokaido & Sanyo Shinkansen Passengers 1972–1987

Year	Passenger Journeys (million)	Passenger-kilometres (billion)	Year	Passenger Journeys (million)	Passenger-kilometres (billion)
1971/72	85.4	26.8	1979/80	123.8	41.0
1972/73*	109.9	33.8	1980/81	125.6	41.7
1973/74	128.1	39.0	1981/82	125.6	41.7
1974/75	133.2	40.7	1982/83	124.8	41.5
1975/76†	157.2	53.3	1983/84	127.6	42.2
1976/77	143.5	48.1	1984/85	128.4	42.2
1977/78	126.8	42.2	1985/86	133.1	43.9
1978/79	123.7	41.1	1986/87	135.1	44.3

* The Sanyo Shinkansen between Osaka and Okayama opened in March 1972.

† The Sanyo Shinkansen between Okayama and Hakata opened in March 1975.

Source: JNR, JR-W

Table 5.2
Tokaido & Sanyo Shinkansen
Numbers of Trains Operated and Coaches in Service
1972–1985

Year	Numbers of Trains per Day			Coaches Owned
	Hikari	Kodama	Total	
1971/72	92	127	219	1164
1972/73*	96	135	231	1344
1973/74	100	135	235	1692
1974/75	120	138	258	2128
1975/76†	120	138	258	2224
1976/77	132	143	275	2336
1977/78	132	143	275	2336
1978/79	132	143	275	2336
1979/80	132	143	275	2336
1980/81	138	117	255	2336
1981/82	138	117	255	2240
1982/83	138	117	255	2240
1983/84	138	117	255	2240
1984/85	149	116	265	2188

* The Sanyo Shinkansen between Osaka and Okayama opened in March 1972.

† The Sanyo Shinkansen between Okayama and Hakata opened in March 1975.

Source: JNR, JR-W

Table 5.3		
Major Sanyo Shinkansen Tunnels		
	Length	
	km	Miles
Rokko	16.250	10.10
Bingo	8.900	5.53
Aki	13.030	8.10
Shin-Kammon	18.713	11.63
Kitakyushu	11.747	7.30

Right: The Type 951 test train which achieved a speed of 286 km/h (177.7 m.p.h.) in 1974. *JR-Central*

Below: Herons continue to fish in the calm waters as a Series 0 *Kodama* crosses the viaduct over the River Yoshii, east of Okayama. *Mikio Miura*

over twice as long again, and the country through which it ran presented the civil engineers with even greater problems. By the chosen route, the gap between Okayama and the new terminus was 244.1 miles (392.8 km), of which more than half (57%) was in tunnel, many being relatively short. All told there are 142 on the whole of the Sanyo Shinkansen. When an observant traveller is making an initial journey over a line, it is usually possible to assess the route that will be used to take it out of a valley. All that happens on the Sanyo Shinkansen, however, is that the tracks head off in the required direction and dive straight into the nearest hillside!

Table 5.3 gives details of the Sanyo Shinkansen's five major tunnels. The longest is the Shin-Kanmon Tunnel which takes the trains under the sea between Honshu and Kyushu. It took four years to construct, and formed another rail link with Kyushu. This island almost closes off the west end of the Inland Sea, leaving a narrow, twisting strait, which at one point is only some 600 metres wide. Tidal flows through this make navigation difficult, and, with the Pacific War pending in the 1940s, it was decided to connect the two separate railway networks by a tunnel between Shimonoseki on the mainland and Moji on Kyushu. This was the Kanmon

Railway Tunnel, 3.6 km (2¼ miles) long, which was completed in June 1942, but only one track was initially provided, the second not being laid until 1944. By contrast the twin-track Shin-Kanmon Tunnel was no less than 18.7 km (11.6 miles) long, in spite of crossing under the strait where it is no wider. However, almost 70% of its length lies below Moji and other built-up areas along the northern coast of Kyushu. Its Honshu portal is situated a long way north-east of the earlier rail tunnel, and the bore swings south-eastwards to cross under the strait, before turning west to continue parallel with the coast until it emerges on to the surface south-west of the earlier tunnels' exit.

Further civil engineering problems faced the Shinkansen after it emerged on to Kyushu. Between Kokura and Hakata there was the 11.7 km (7.3-mile) Kitakyushu Tunnel to bore, but potentially more serious was the requirement to restrict speed to 110 km/h (68 m.p.h.) for the rest of the way to the terminus. This was because the area traversed had been mined extensively for coal in the past. Although these workings had been abandoned, the positions of some of them had not been recorded, and for safety reasons speed was restricted. (The French high-speed line to Lille, which

Right: In 1992 a *West Hikari* passes Fukuyama Castle. *Mikio Miura*

Below left: One of the plaques, applied in June 1996, for the Series 951 test train used on the Sanyo Shinkansen, commemorating the speed of 286 km/h (177.7 m.p.h.) it achieved on 24 February 1974. *Mikio Miura*

Below right: One of the Sanyo Series 0 sets in later years operating a *West Hikari* service. Note how the coach number has been lined up with the marker on the track. *Mikio Miura*

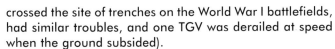

crossed the site of trenches on the World War I battlefields, had similar troubles, and one TGV was derailed at speed when the ground subsided).

Elsewhere at this time environmental opposition to the Shinkansen had resulted in a case against JNR which might have resulted in the high-speed trains being slowed to less than a third of their design speed for several miles through Nagoya. This was finally settled, with the aid of some financial compensation, in September 1980. The noise problem, however, was significantly to affect the construction of further high-speed lines in Japan, as described in the next chapter.

It is not surprising that all this civil engineering work pushed up the cost of building the Sanyo Shinkansen, the final bill working out at approximately ¥910 billion. On a mile-for-mile basis this was over 2½ times that for the New Tokaido Line. (¥2.6 billion/mile compared with ¥1.0 billion).

When the whole of the Sanyo Shinkansen came into service on 10 March 1975, it was possible to travel by high-speed train continuously for 664.3 miles (1069.1 km), some five miles further than the journey from London King's Cross to Brora in Sutherland, via York, Edinburgh, Perth and Inverness. The best Tokyo–Hakata journey time initially was 6hr 56min, but this was cut to 6hr 40min after 1980, giving an overall average of 99.6 m.p.h. (160.3 km/h). Maximum speeds throughout were limited to the standard 210 km/h (131 m.p.h.). A 5H-5K service pattern was adopted over the Tokaido stretch of the route.

Between Okayama and Hakata the high-speed line had nine new intermediate stations. This gave an average spacing of 39 km (24 miles), which was marginally longer than the 32 km (20 mile) average for the stretch between Shin-Osaka and Okayama. Even after the opening of Mishima station (between Atami and Shizuoka) on the Tokaido Shinkansen in 1969, the average station spacing on that line was 43km (27 miles). (Three additional intermediate stations on this line were opened in March 1988, at Shin-Fuji, Kakegawa and Mikawa-Anjo). By subsequent European high-speed railway standards these gaps were small, as the first French TGV line had only two intermediate stations served by the high-speed trains in the 426 km (265 miles) between Paris and Lyon. On 'Britain's Fastest Railway', the East Coast InterCity trains only serve 14 stations on the 632 km (393 mile) stretch from King's Cross to Edinburgh.

In 1982 the author had the opportunity to observe the operation of a Series 0 set between Fukuyama and Hiroshima from the cab. Under normal conditions, trains were able to keep time by running at 10 km/h (6 m.p.h.) less than line speed, which gave a small recovery margin. As mentioned earlier, there was no cruise-control, and, with gradients as steep as 1 in 83 to contend with, considerable skill was needed to maintain the required speed without dropping time or causing the ATC to take action if the train went too fast. This was particularly noticeable over the switchbacks between Mihara and Hiroshima. It needed full power to maintain 120 m.p.h. (193 km/h) up the 12-mile bank to km post 790, but once over the top we were able to maintain the same rate of progress down the similar inclination through the 8-mile Aki Tunnel with power shut off.

The km posts with their reflective paint showed up clearly as we rushed through that long bore, and suddenly our ears popped. A Tokyo-bound train had entered the other end, and far ahead we could spot the tiny pin-pricks of its headlights. As we approached at a closing speed of 260 m.p.h. (420 km/h) the lights rapidly grew larger and then the train flashed past us. The flicker of sparks from its pantographs was clearly apparent from our elevated position in the cab, with the bright patches of illumination from its windows passing below us.

Out in the open air the experience was very different, with the exhilaration of rushing over viaducts high above the landscape for much of the journey. Aided by the shape of the windscreen and the smooth ride, at times it felt as if we were in a low-flying aircraft, which even 'banked' to change direction. Coming into Hiroshima there was a particularly long viaduct across part of the flourishing city, rebuilt after being at the receiving-end of the first atomic bomb, with vast 'Japanese-gauge' railway yards and running lines on both sides.

The opening of the Hakata extension in March 1975 came close on the heels of the Middle-East oil crisis. Although, at the time, this was expected to improve the railways' transport share, the world recession that followed affected the Japanese high-speed lines. Table 5.1 shows how, in 1975/76, the year that followed the opening to Hakata, Shinkansen passenger numbers reached a peak of 157.2 million. There was a then dramatic drop for the next two years, after which loadings bottomed out at around 125 million. Twelve years were to elapse before the 1975/76 figures were again achieved.

There was no increase in the average number of trains worked each day after the extension to Hakata came into use, but it will be seen from Table 5.2 that the coaching-stock fleet was enlarged. The total built up from 1164 before the extension to Okayama opened to 2336 in the year after the Hakata services began. This total then remained constant for the next eight years, after which there was a slight fall. With the opening to Hakata, the basic train service over the Tokaido Shinkansen became a 5H-5K one, which was to last until the autumn of 1986. There were initially some 23 daily trains which operated west of Osaka, but the following year this number increased to 40.

As shown in Table 5.4, however, the profitability of the extended high-speed line still continued to improve, even during the recession, rising by 35% from 1975/76 to 1977/78, whereas passenger numbers fell by 20%. Fares were increased nine times between 1974 and 1985 (inclusive), and operating expenses rose too, but it was not until the autumn of 1979 that the *Kodama* train formations were cut to 12 coaches as an economy measure. Total JNR losses being carried forward had by then reached approximately ¥12 trillion, which made the Shinkansen's ¥248 billion profit look like small change.

Hakata has long been an important part of the city of Fukuoka, but the station still retains its original name. In April 1990 services using Shinkansen stock were extended for a further five miles (8½ km) from Hakata to Hakata-Minami (Hakata South) station. This is

the location of the train depot on Kyushu, and it was decided to use the connecting line for local passengers at 'ordinary' speeds. These workings are operated by four- or six-car Series 0 shuttles.

The world railway speed survey published every other year by *Railway Gazette International* from 1975 enables us to see how Japanese speeds have changed since then. Table 5.5 lists the fastest start-to-stop averages between stations from 1975 until 1985 on the combined Tokaido and Sanyo Shinkansen. It will be seen that there were two significant increases. Between 1975 and 1977 the fastest speed rose from 105.4 to 110.3 m.p.h. (169.6 to 177.5 km/h) and there was a smaller rise to 112.4 m.p.h. (180.9 km/h) between 1979 and 1981. No figures are available for these two lines in 1987, as the Tohoku and Joetsu Shinkansen entries occupied all the spaces in the Japanese section of the table, following the increase in the maximum speed on those routes. Japan occupied first place in the world table until the first TGV line opened fully in the autumn of 1983, but the SNCF has never operated anything like as many fast trains as the New Tokaido Line.

The fastest Shinkansen journey times, inclusive of intermediate stops, are shown in Table 5.6, which goes right up to 1987, with an entry for the New Sanyo Line that year. That was actually faster than the best start-to-stop speed in the table two years earlier. Both the 1985 and 1987 entries involved trains running over the Sanyo Shinkansen.

The various tables in this chapter take the statistics to the end of the nationalised JNR era, and we will be considering the very significant subsequent improvements in later chapters.

Table 5.4
**Tokaido+Sanyo Shinkansen Revenue and Expenses
1972–1987**
(Billions of Yen)

Year	Revenue	Expenses§	Profit/Loss
1971/72	199	91	108
1972/73*	251	125	126
1973/74	290	135	155
1974/75	326	169	157
1975/76†	478	295	183
1976/77	547	328	218
1977/78	616	368	248
1978/79	652	372	280
1979/80	699	397	302
1980/81	729	433	299

* The Sanyo Shinkansen between Osaka and Okayama opened in March 1972.
† The Sanyo Shinkansen between Okayama and Hakata opened in March 1975.
§ Including interest and depreciation.

Source: *The Privatisation of Railways in Japan*, East Japan Railway Culture Foundation (1985).

Table 5.5
Fastest Tokaido+Sanyo Shinkansen Start-to-Stop Speeds 1975–1985

Year	Train	From*	To*	Distance km	miles	Time min	Speed km/h	m.p.h.
1975	104 *Hikari*	Tokyo	Nagoya	324.0	201.3	121	169.6	105.4
1977	1 *Hikari*	Nagoya	Shizouka	174.6	108.5	59	177.5	110.3
1979	1 *Hikari*	Nagoya	Shizouka	174.6	108.5	59	177.5	110.3
1981	1 *Hikari*	Nagoya	Yokohama	316.5	196.7	105	180.9	112.4
1983	1 *Hikari*	Nagoya	Yokohama	316.5	196.7	105	180.9	112.4
1985	2 *Hikari*	Hiroshima	Okayama	144.9	90.0	48	181.1	112.5

* Some of the multiple journeys may be in the opposite direction.

Source: *Railway Gazette International*.

24

The author's 1982 visit to Japan came 18 months after he had taken over the 'Locomotive Practice & Performance' series in *The Railway Magazine*. This had first appeared in 1901, and had become the longest-running railway series in the world. With commercial services having just begun on the first TGV line, it was interesting to be able to publish examples of the latest practice and performance on the Japanese Shinkansen, which had, by then, been in operation for nearly 18 years. After business discussions in Osaka had been completed, we set out westwards along the Sanyo Shinkansen on *Hikari 61*, which left Shin-Osaka at 07.07, the journey beginning with breakfast in the dining-car, before we adjourned to the cab.

The log of the run is given in Table 5.7. There are relatively few intermediate stations, but I discovered it was possible to use the km posts on the overhead-electrification masts for timing purposes, although it was not always possible to spot those on the near side at speed. Accordingly the log only gives the average speeds between timing points. The speed restriction through Shin-Kobe had its effect on the opening section from Osaka, but we then maintained fairly even progress over the next three stretches to Aioi, before slowing for the Okayama stop. We arrived there nine seconds inside schedule, having averaged 103.6 m.p.h (166.7 km/h) start-to-stop from Shin-Osaka. Some of the following timekeeping was not quite so good, but we nevertheless succeeded in averaging more than 100 m.p.h. start-to-stop over both the longer runs.

Our climb to the summit at km post 790 and the subsequent descent through Aki Tunnel provided me with an opportunity to assess our train's power output. Down the 1 in 83 through the tunnel with power off, we had maintained a steady 120 m.p.h. (193 km/h), so the 8200 h.p. being produced by gravity on our 950 tonne train was sufficient to overcome the aerodynamic and rolling resistance. The latter included that needed to keep the 64 traction motors turning over. This corresponded to 640 h.p. at that speed, and, when deducted from the total, left a figure of 7560 h.p. On the earlier climb, with the controller fully open, speed had steadied out at the same speed up the long 1 in 83 bank, so the total power being produced by the traction motors then worked out as 15 760hp (7560 + 8200), which was remarkably close to the installed capacity of 15 840hp for our 16-coach train.

High-speed running in long tunnels needs more power than in open country. However, the large twin-track bores on the Shinkansen do not exact anything like the same penalty as the Eurotunnel Shuttles experience, because the Japanese trains do not occupy anything like the same proportion of the cross-sectional area. (The same large diameter can be seen in the North Downs Tunnel on the British Channel Tunnel Rail Link, holed through in June 2000). Some comparative figures were available for one of the 12-car Series 200 trains that had just started operating on the Tohoku Shinkansen. These sets are more powerful than the Series 0s, but sufficient motors had been cut out on that particular test to give the same power:weight ratio. On a 1 in 87 rising gradient, the newer train had a balancing speed of 118 m.p.h. (190 km/h) in tunnel, compared with 121 (195 km/h) in the open.

Table 5.6
Fastest Tokaido+Sanyo Shinkansen Journeys, inclusive of intermediate stops 1975–1987

Year	Train	From*	To*	Distance km	miles	Time hr	min	No. of Stops	Speed km/h	mph
1975	100 Hikari	Tokyo	Osaka	515.4	320.3	3	10	2	162.8	101.2
1977	107 Hikari	Tokyo	Osaka	515.4	320.3	3	10	2	162.8	101.2
1979	107 Hikari	Tokyo	Osaka	515.4	320.3	3	10	2	162.8	101.2
1981	90 Hikari	Tokyo	Osaka	515.4	320.3	3	10	2	162.8	101.2
1983	90 Hikari	Tokyo	Osaka	515.4	320.3	3	10	2	162.8	101.2
1985	11 Hikari	Tokyo	Hiroshima	821.3	510.3	4	56	4	166.5	103.5
1987	1 Hikari	Hakata	Osaka	553.7	344.1	3	02	3	182.5	113.4

* Some of the multiple journeys may be in the opposite direction.

Source: *Railway Gazette International.*

Table 5.7
JNR: SANYO SHINKANSEN SHIN-OSAKA–OGORI

Date	5 August 1982
Stock	Series 0
Load: No/empty/full(tons)	16/882/950

Distances Miles	km		Schedule min.	Actual m	s	Speeds* m.p.h.	km/h
0.0	0.0	SHIN-OSAKA	0	0	00	–	–
20.2	32.5	Shin-Kobe		12	51	94.3	151.8
34.0	54.7	Nishiakashi		20	16	111.6	179.6
53.3	85.8	Himeji		30	33	112.6	181.2
65.8	105.9	Aioi		37	19	110.8	178.3
99.9	160.1	OKAYAMA	58	57	51	99.6	160.3
16.0	25.7	Shin-Kurashiki		10	59	87.5	140.8
35.3	56.8	FUKUYAMA	22	22	48	97.7	157.2
24.2	38.9	km post 772		14	09	102.6	165.1
34.7	55.8	km post 789		19	14	120.0	193.1
44.6	71.8	km post 805		24	09	125.0	201.1
50.2	80.8	km post 814		26	58	119.3	192.0
54.7	88.0	HIROSHIMA	33	32	11	51.8	83.4
27.4	44.1	Shin-Iwakuni		16	09	101.8	163.8
51.1	82.2	Tokuyama		28	50	112.1	180.4
76.6	123.3	OGORI	43	44	22	98.5	158.5

* Averages from previous timing point.

Source: *The Railway Magazine*, December 1982.

Anniversaries & Celebrations

Top: 20th Anniversary Special for the opening of the Tokaido Shinkansen passes Gifu-Hashima with its commemorative 'headboard', 1 October 1984.   *Mikio Miura*

Below: The stamps on a commemorative postcard for the 30th Anniversary of the opening of the Tokaido Shinkansen. The one showing the Series 0 train was issued in 1964, and has been franked with the 30th Anniversary special cancellation.

Above: Sticker on side of *Kodama* which was used extensively in October 1994 to mark the 30th Anniversary of the Tokaido Shinkansen's opening.   *Mikio Miura*

Top right: Commemorative tickets issued at Kamonomiya station on 23 June 1982 to mark the 20th Anniversary of the opening of the Shinkansen Test Track. From top to bottom they show:
  1. The 'A' prototype train with President Sogo waving from its cab.
  2. A Series 0 passing Mount Fuji.
  3. Commemorative medals and plaques.
(The date shown on the ticket stubs [57-7-2] is an example of the old system used in Japan, which started again with the accession of each emperor, in this case Emperor Hirohito).

Right: Series 0 Shinkansen in Tokyo Central station with 'head-board' to mark the beginning of 'Privatisation' on 31 March 1987.   *Mikio Miura*

Extreme right: The launching party, each with their gold ceremonial scissors to cut the ribbon, stand beside a Series 100 Shinkansen ready for the ceremony of 'Breaking the Ball' to mark the beginning of Central Japan Railway on 31 March 1987. *JR-Central*

2両編成で試運転する新幹線（昭和37年頃）

十河国鉄総裁（昭和37年頃）

（見　本）

鴨　宮　駅

普通入場券　120円

旅客車内に立ち入ることはできません。　までの間に1回限り有効

57-7-2

57-6.23

昭和57年6月
新幹線発祥20周年記念

新幹線と富士山（東田子の浦附近）

（見　本）

鴨　宮　駅

普通入場券　60円

旅客車内に立ち入ることはできません。　までの間に1回限り有効

57-7-2

57-6.23

昭和57年6月
新幹線発祥20周年記念

新幹線記念碑
（東京駅）

コロンブス賞
（国鉄本社）

新幹線
発祥記念碑
（鴨宮）

（見　本）

鴨　宮　駅

普通入場券　120円

旅客車内に立ち入ることはできません。　までの間に1回限り有効

57-7-2

57-6.23

昭和57年6月
新幹線発祥20周年記念

CHAPTER 6
The Network Grows

In 1969 the New Comprehensive National Development Plan was approved by the Japanese cabinet, which included the construction of a Shinkansen network with a total length of 7200 km (4500 miles). Although at that time only the original 515 km (320 miles) of the Tokaido Shinkansen were in being, and a start had been made on the Sanyo extension, the whole network was planned to be completed by 1985. In the following year the Japanese Diet (parliament) enacted a Law for the Construction of Nationwide High-Speed Railways, which aimed 'to construct a nationwide high-speed railway network to promote the growth of the national economy and to enlarge people's sphere of activity'.

On this basis, plans were decided, on the dates shown, for the following additional lines:

Date	Name	Route
January 1971	Tohoku	Tokyo to Morioka in northern Honshu.
	Joetsu	Tokyo to Niigata on the coast of the Sea of Japan.
	Narita	Tokyo to Narita International Airport.
June 1972	Tohoku	Morioka to Amori on the north coast of Honshu.
	Hokkaido	Amori to Sapporo through the Seikan Tunnel.
	Hokuriku	Tokyo to Osaka via Toyama on north coast of Honshu.
	Kyushu	Hakata to Kagoshima, with a branch to Nagasaki.

In April 1971 JNR and the Japan Railway Construction Public Corporation were instructed to start work on the first two of these projects, which were estimated to cost ¥880 billion and ¥580 billion respectively.

Meanwhile opposition was growing from those living close to the existing Shinkansen, who were finding the noise and vibration from the growing number of trains oppressive. In December 1972 the Environmental Agency recommended that noise in residential areas should not exceed 80 dBA, and special protective measures were to be taken where it was greater than 85 dBA. This involved the construction of lineside walls almost 2 metres high. Just after the opening of the Hakata extension in 1975, even stricter noise-suppression measures were announced by the Central Council for Environmental Pollution. Retrospectively it would be impossible to meet these on the existing routes, but the new lines would have to comply.

These requirements pushed up the construction cost considerably, and by 1975 the estimate for the Tohoku Line as far as Morioka had risen to ¥1593 billion, just as the Middle East oil crisis began to bite. With no oil supplies of their own, the whole Japanese economy was particularly vulnerable to the rapid increases in the price of fuel. That year it was announced that the completion of the Tohoku Line would be postponed from 1977 to 1979, and work on it actually stopped at one point.

The 65km (40-mile) Narita Line was overwhelmed by the massive protests against noise from the proposed new Tokyo international airport. Work had begun on that rail link in 1974, but progressed no further than the construction of a shell for the airport station and a short length of viaduct setting off towards Tokyo. Nationally the importance of the airport was much greater than a short high-speed railway connection to the capital, and the latter was dropped. That decision was helped by the fact that the private Keisei Electric Railway had already built its own line to the airport, and had purchased some *Skyliner* trains for the route. So, when the airport opened in 1978 it was served by this private line, and it was not until 1991 that East Japan Railway started to operate its 'Narita Express' service from various Tokyo stations, including platforms at Central which are five levels down. For the final few minutes of their journey to the airport, the latter's well-appointed EMUs, running on 'Japanese-gauge' tracks, climb on to the short stretch of the viaduct originally built for the Shinkansen link. They then terminate in the spacious underground platforms whose layout was derived from the abortive high-speed project of the 1970s.

The Japanese, as well as their economy, are resilient, and quick to adapt to changing circumstances. To meet the new constraints, Omiya, some 20 miles (30 km) from the centre of Tokyo, would be used as the temporary terminus for both the new northern Shinkansen routes. Originally it had been intended that the Joetsu would have its own terminus in the Shinjuku area of Tokyo. Omiya was a busy station on the Old Tohoku Line, but that was as close as they could get into the capital in the current environmental climate. A 'Japanese-gauge' 'Shinkansen Relay' service was operated between Ueno and Omiya, with a journey time of about 25 minutes, after passengers had used a suburban service between Tokyo Central and the busy, two-level, station at Ueno.

The designers of the Tohoku Line managed to avoid building more than four viaducts more than 700 metres long, the details of these being given in Table 6.1. Kitakamigawa No.1 bridge, between the stations of Ichinoseki and

---

Table 6.1
Major Tohoku Shinkansen Viaducts and Tunnels
Viaducts (over 700m)

	Length	
	Metres	Yards
Kitakamigawa No.1	3868	4230
Kitakamigawa No.2	1025	2734
Tonegawa	819	896
Kinugawa	763	834

Longest 10 Tunnels

	Length	
	Metres	Yards
Fukushima	11 700	12 801
Zao	11 215	12 265
Ichinoseki	9730	10 641
Nasu	7030	7688
Shiroishi No.2	3738	4088
Shiga	3502	3830
Osaki	3065	3352
Shirasaka	2965	3423
Ishikurayama	2620	2865
Arikabe No.2	2428	2655

Source: JNR

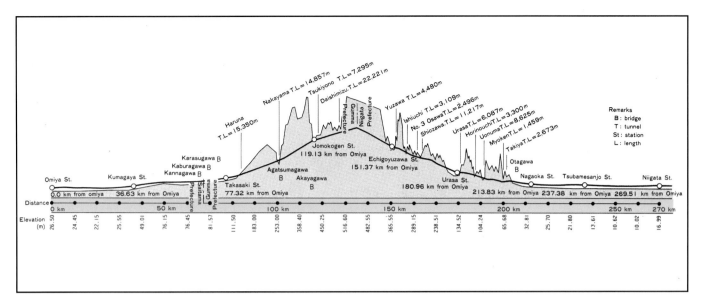

Longitudinal profile of Joetsu Shinkansen. *Provided by JR-East*

Mizusawa-Esashi, roughly half-way between Sendai and Morioka, is Japan's longest, and spanned a wide valley. A truss section was used for nearly 600 metres across the river, with reinforced concrete beams for the rest. The usual sound-suppression walls were provided throughout, as described below. Tunnels on the Tohoku Line were a different story, and even the tenth longest stretched for more than a mile and a half. The lengths of these ten are also given in the table. Construction was relatively straightforward, however, unlike those on the Joetsu Line, as we will see later.

Noise suppression was extremely important along the whole length of the new routes, and a section of the Tohoku Line, 43 km (27 miles) long, was initially constructed between the city of Kuki and Ishibashi, where trials were carried out to test different ways of reducing the spread of sound from the trains, particularly that generated by the running-gear. The most effective arrangement was found to be side walls, 2.2 metres (7¼ feet) high, which come almost to the level of the train windows, and have a top ledge overhanging inwards and supported by a series of struts. The need to construct hundreds of miles of these put the cost up considerably, but, in the longer run, they were to permit trains to run faster without causing an unacceptable level of protest. However, the final cost of the new line worked out at ¥2800 billion – one and three-quarters times the original estimate, which on a mile-for-mile basis was more than 7½ times that of the Tokaido Line.

Slab track was used nearly everywhere, except at turnouts. The same track parameters were adopted as those used on the Sanyo Shinkansen, but the detail of the signalling system was considerably different. Block sections were only 1.2 km long (almost three-quarters of a mile), but speed started to be reduced from 210 km/h four blocks before the required stopping point. This distance totalled only 4.8 km, compared with the 6.0 km on the original Tokaido Line, but there was still an adequate safety factor. Table 6.2 shows the distances necessary to stop from dif-

ferent speeds under service and emergency conditions. It will be seen that even from 240 km/h (149 m.p.h.), 4100 metres (4500 yd) is sufficient to stop using a service application, while 'putting the anchors out' would bring a train to a halt in just 3000 metres (3300 yd).

All this extra work and expense put back the completion of the two new lines, and neither was opened until 1982. Commercial services began on the Tohoku Shinkansen in June that year, but it was not until the November that the Joetsu Shinkansen opened for business. This was a shorter line, only 269.5 km (167.5 miles) long, but it had to traverse the Mikuni mountain range.

To get through the ridge 13 tunnels were needed, the longest being the 22.221-km (13.81-mile) Daishimizu Tunnel, which was then the longest railway tunnel in the world. That was a major job in itself, but the shorter, 14.8-km (9.2-mile), Nakayama Tunnel, somewhat further south, had to be driven through volcanic rocks from which the workers discovered that streams of high-pressure water could emerge. As well as boring it from both ends, three intermediate shafts were dug, one of them 372 metres (1220 ft) deep. The inrush of water twice completely flooded the workings and forced an alignment change, whose curves are sharp enough to require a 160 km/h (100 m.p.h.) speed restriction. The so-called New Austrian Tunnelling Method (NATM) was used for the first time in Japan on a large scale to deal with the worst ground, which was so bad that in places twin small side-wall bores had to be bored first before opening them out to produce the full-sized running tunnel. (The method of constructing the UK Cross-over Cavern in the Channel Tunnel was not dissimilar). Ten years were needed to complete the Nakayama Tunnel, which was only finished in 1982.

Altogether tunnels occupy 39% of the Joetsu Line's length. Table 6.3 lists its ten longest bores, as well as the two viaducts over 700 metres long. Although too short to appear in the table, Akayagawa Bridge, between the north portal of Nakayama Tunnel and Jomokogen station, is a particularly fine one. It spans a river and road at a noted beauty spot, and was constructed as a reinforced-concrete arch. Its span of 116 metres (380 ft) made it the longest railway arch in the world.

Snowdrifts up to 4 metres (13 ft) deep occur in the mountains traversed by the Joetsu Line, and snow-sheds had to be built to protect the line from avalanches. Sprinkler sys-

Table 6.2					
Stopping Distances on Tohoku and Joetsu Shinkansen					
Initial Speed		**Service Stop**		**Emergency Stop**	
km/h	**m.p.h.**	**Metres**	**Yards**	**Metres**	**Yards**
220	137	3300	3600	2500	2750
240	149	4100	4500	3000	3300
Source: JNR					

Table 6.3
Major Joetsu Shinkansen Viaducts and Tunnels
Viaducts (over 700m)

	Length	
	Metres	Yards
Karasugawa	1380	1509
Kannagawa	746	816

Longest 10 Tunnels

	Length	
	Metres	Yards
Daishimizu	22 221	24 301
Haruna	15 350	16 787
Nakayama	14 857	16 248
Shiozawa	11 020	12 051
Tsukiyono	7295	7978
Urasa	6023	6587
Yumoto	4455	4872
Uonuma	3624	3963
Horinouchi	3190	3489
Ishiuchi	3093	3383

Source: JNR

tems beside the tracks, using water at about 10° C, were needed at numerous points along both the new routes to melt fresh snowfalls, and the new trains had small snow-ploughs added to the front faring below their bullet-noses.

In view of all the engineering problems, it is not surprising that the cost per mile for the Joetsu Shinkansen was higher even than that of the Tohoku Line, and worked out at nearly ¥9 billion/mile. The final total of ¥1630 billion was roughly three times that originally estimated (¥580 billion). Included in the cost were the usual earthquake warning arrangements, but these were supplemented by distant seismometers on the coast to detect shock waves from below the Pacific Ocean.

Public services on the Tohoku Shinkansen commenced in June 1982, but it was not until the November of that year that the Joetsu route was ready to begin revenue operation. As on the earlier lines, the timetable for each route included two different sorts of train – those making limited stops and those calling at all stations. On the Tohoku Shinkansen the former were called Yamabiko ('Mountain Echo') and the latter Aoba ('Green Leaves'). The corresponding names on the Joetsu Shinkansen are Asahi ('Morning Sun') and Toki ('Crested Ibis').

Agreement on how to extend the high-speed line into Ueno station, a distance of 27.7 km (17.2 miles), had not been reached until 1978, and, although some construction work had commenced by the time the lines were opened, it was not until March 1985 that Ueno became the starting point for through Shinkansen services to Niigata and Morioka. Coming south from Omiya the line was built on a continuous viaduct, high above the suburbs. Ballastless track covered with resilient material, known as Danchoku in technician's language, was used to reduce vibration and noise, and speed is limited to 110 km/h (68 m.p.h.).

One of the perennial objections to a high-speed line (or motorway) is that those who suffer the environmental disadvantages do not have the opportunity to use the new facility as there are no intermediate access points (stations for the railway or slip-roads in the case of motorways). As a quid pro quo, the 'Japanese-gauge' Saikyo Line was built alongside the Shinkansen for much of the way between Omiya and Ueno, and various intermediate stations provided. Another trade-off was the construction of a rubber-tyred link for the Saitama New City Transport system along-

side the Joetsu Shinkansen for 12.7 km (7.9 miles) northwards from Omiya. Tunnelling in the Ueno area was difficult and there was a bad collapse at one point, with a number of fatalities, and complications caused by an unidentified car of foreign manufacture in the hole!

At the same time as the Ueno extension came into operation, the maximum speed on the Tohoku and Joetsu Shinkansen was raised to 240 km/h (149 m.p.h.), which made the Yamabiko and Asahi services the fastest in Japan. Again great care was taken to ensure that the higher speeds did not decrease safety standards, and trial runs had begun as early as September 1983. In October 1984 a Type 925 test train successfully reached 261 km/h (162 m.p.h.) between Fukushima and Koriyama on the Tohoku Line, and a year later the same train pushed the speed to 272 km/h (169 m.p.h.), as shown in Table 10.2. In November 1986 a test run with a standard set reached 271 km/h. From the beginning the Tohoku and Joetsu Shinkansen had their own Central Control Centre, comparable to the original one, and situated only a short distance away, with all the same COMTRAC facilities as before.

To give the required stopping distance at this higher service speed, a further three 'block sections' were added to the ATC system, during which speed is brought down to the old maximum of 210 km/h, after which the usual reductions occur, successively to 160, 110 and 30 km/h (100, 68 and 19 m.p.h.). In total, therefore, there is now a distance of 8,400 metres (9200 yd) in which to make a conventional stop, and, as shown in Table 6.2, the units are capable of achieving this in no more than 4100 metres with nothing fiercer than a service application. The speed can be controlled at other intermediate levels for curves, etc. The ATC system on these two new routes differed from that on the Tokaido and Sanyo Shinkansen in having a dual-frequency system of coded track-circuits, and this assisted the task of increasing the line speed. We will see later how the journey times were reduced by these higher speeds and the change of terminus.

Ueno was still not the ultimate goal of the northern Shinkansen, which wanted to reach Tokyo Central. There was no question of any inter-running with the Tokaido Line, because such an operation was, at that time, prevented by the two different power-supply frequencies, but it was clearly commercially important for the country's two premier services to start from the capital's same central station. Finding space to thread the pair of Standard-gauge tracks through the 3.6 km (2¼-mile) gap was not easy, and after work had started in 1981, it was stopped two years later.

Series 200 Rolling Stock

To operate the Tohoku and Joetsu Shinkansen, a new generation of 'multiple-unit' trains was constructed, the Series 200 sets. Externally there were two changes from the Tokaido 'Bullet Trains' whose image was by then recognised worldwide. The first was the most obvious, with the blue and cream livery being replaced by a striking green and cream one. Their 'bullet-noses' were also lengthened slightly, and sets were nicknamed 'Long-Nose Beauties'. The interiors were much more attractive than those of the Series 0 sets at that time, with white net curtains being provided in the Green Cars, as well as the usual opaque ones. There was a buffet car, which also had external access for wheel-chair passengers. Each of the 12-car sets accommodated 833 ordinary passengers, with 52 in the single Green Car. The seat pitch was longer than on the earlier Series 0 cars, which added to the comfort.

An early 1980s view of a Series 200 on one of the long, low viaducts of the Tohoku Shinkansen. The feeder cables for the 2 x 25 kV overhead system are suspended by insulators hanging from the brackets fixed to the tops of the concrete masts. Closer to the mast tops are the earthing cables connected to the flash-over arrestors on the low-tension ends of the insulators.

From a technical point of view, however, there were a lot of differences from the earlier Tokaido Line trains. Light alloys were used for the bodyshells, rather than steel, and the underfloor equipment was shrouded to prevent the build-up of snow. The roof-grilles which were a feature of the Series 0 trains also disappeared, and alternative intakes for the air-conditioning were provided high up on the body sides. To prevent the 'wrong sort of snow' entering the equipment, an unusual separating device was fitted inside each of these grilles. They can be described as miniature versions of the horn on an old-fashioned acoustic gramophone, and fling the snow centrifugally outwards as the air-flow is turned through 180° and the tapering bore increases its speed. This enables the snow to be extracted by a small ejector, which forces it back into the atmosphere before it can reach the main intake fan. Small equipment spaces were required at the coach-ends to accommodate this equipment, slightly reducing the seating capacity compared with the Series 0 cars. All these additions increased the weight of the coaches, in spite of the use of light alloys, and the maximum axle-load went up to 17 tonnes.

To enable the required speeds to be maintained up the 1 in 83 gradients of the Joetsu Line, higher-powered motors were provided, with a rating of 230 kW (310 h.p.) per axle. They were still of the well-proven series-wound d.c. type, but their power supply came from thyristor bridges, rather than tap-changers. They thus correspond to the system used on the British Class 90s, rather than our original

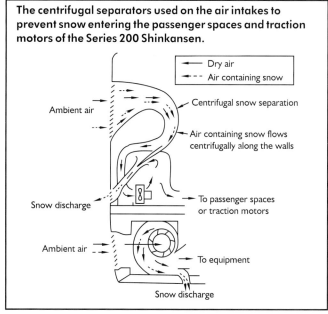

The centrifugal separators used on the air intakes to prevent snow entering the passenger spaces and traction motors of the Series 200 Shinkansen.

Table 6.4
Tohoku & Joetsu Shinkansen Train-sets 1982–1986

	Cars			Sets			
Year	New	Total	E	F	G	Total	Comments
1980	108	108	9	-	-	9	For test running and service on Tohoku Line.
1981	264	372	31	-	-	31	For service on Joetsu and Tohoku Lines.
1982	60	432	36	-	-	36	For increased services.
1983	36	468	36	3	-	39	F sets had maximum speed raised to 240 km/h (149 mph)
1984	192	660	36	19	-	55	For start of services from Ueno.
1985	24	684	36	21	-	57	For increased services.
1986	4	688	20	29	10	59	Control cars with new profile.

Source: JR-E

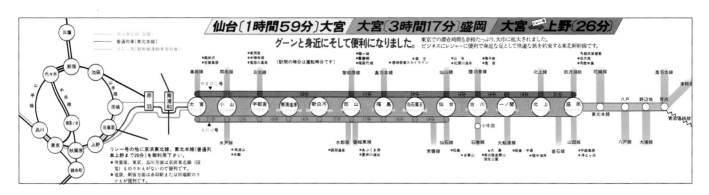

Centre timetable — 新幹線 上り (Up direction):

列車名	あおば 200号	やまびこ 10号	やまびこ 50号	あおば 202号	やまびこ 12号	やまびこ 14号	あおば 204号	やまびこ 52号	あおば 206号	やまびこ 16号	あおば 208号	やまびこ 18号	あおば 210号	やまびこ 20号
盛岡 発	……	715	……	……	1020	1115	……	……	……	1515	……	1720	……	1915
北上 〃	……	736	……	……	1041	1136	……	……	……	1536	……	1741	……	1936
一ノ関 〃	……	755	……	……	1100	1155	……	……	……	1555	……	1800	……	1955
古川 〃	……	814	……	……	1119	1214	……	……	……	1614	……	1819	……	2014
仙台 着	……	831	……	……	1136	1231	……	……	……	1631	……	1836	……	2031
仙台 発	640	833	930	1315	1138	1233	1315	1400	1515	1633	1725	1838	1910	2033
白石蔵王 〃	659	↓	↓	1334	↓	1334	↓	534	1534	↓	1744	↓	1929	↓
福島 〃	715	903	1000	1350	1208	1303	1350	1430	1550	1703	1800	1908	1945	2103
郡山 〃	733	921	1018	1108	1226	1321	1408	1448	608	1721	1818	1926	2003	2121
新白河 〃	749	↓	↓	1124	↓	1424	↓	624	↓	1834	↓	2019	↓	
那須塩原 〃	803	↓	↓	1138	↓	1438	↓	638	↓	1848	↓	2033	↓	
宇都宮 〃	822	1001	1058	1157	1306	1401	1457	1528	657	1801	1907	2006	2052	2201
小山 〃	836	↓	↓	1211	↓	1511	↓	711	↓	1921	↓	2106	↓	
大宮 着	857	1032	1129	1232	1337	1432	1532	1559	732	1832	1942	2037	2127	2232

連絡列車専用 リレー号	2号	4号	6号	8号	10号	12号	14号	16号	18号	20号	22号	24号	26号	28号
大宮 発	911	1047	1145	1246	1353	453	1547	1616	1753	1847	1957	2056	2144	2250
上野 着	937	1113	1210	1313	1419	519	1613	1642	1819	1913	2023	2121	2210	2316

Centre timetable — 新幹線 下り (Down direction):

連絡列車専用 リレー号	1号	普通列車	3号	5号	7号	9号	11号	13号	15号	17号	19号	21号	23号	25号
上野 発	633	739	830	930	1030	1130	1224	1339	1433	1536	1630	1700	1837	1950
大宮 着	659	805	855	955	1055	1155	1249	1405	1459	1602	1655	1726	1903	2015

列車名	やまびこ 11号	あおば 201号	やまびこ 13号	あおば 203号	やまびこ 15号	あおば 51号	やまびこ 53号	あおば 205号	やまびこ 17号	あおば 207号	やまびこ 19号	あおば 209号	やまびこ 21号	あおば 211号
大宮 発	715	820	915	1015	1115	1215	1315	1420	1515	1620	1715	1745	1925	2030
小山 〃	↓	841	↓	1036	↓	↓	1336	↓	↓	1641	↓	1806	↓	2051
宇都宮 〃	746	913	946	1049	1146	1246	1349	1451	1546	1654	1746	1838	1956	2123
那須塩原 〃	↓	927	↓	1108	↓	↓	1408	↓	↓	1713	↓	1852	↓	2137
新白河 〃	↓	↓	↓	1122	↓	↓	1422	↓	↓	1727	↓	↓	↓	2150
郡山 〃	826	943	1026	1138	1226	1326	1438	1531	1626	1743	1826	1908	2036	2153
福島 〃	845	1002	1045	1157	1245	1345	1457	1550	1645	1802	1845	1927	2055	2212
白石蔵王 〃	↓	1018	↓	1213	↓	↓	1513	↓	↓	1818	↓	1943	↓	2228
仙台 着	914	1037	1114	1232	1314	1414	1532	1619	1714	1837	1914	2002	2124	2247
仙台 発	……		1116		1316				1716		1916		2126	
古川 〃	933		1133		1333				1733		1933		2143	
一ノ関 〃	952		1152		1352				1752		1952		2202	
北上 〃	1011		1211		1411				1811		2011		2221	
盛岡 着	1032		1232		1432				1832		2032		2242	

記事: 7/2から運転 ほか

Top: A 1984 route diagram for the new Tohoku Shinkansen, showing its connections with the loop formed by the Yamanote Line in central Tokyo. The figures between the dots by the stations show the running times over those stretches for the *Aoba* trains (green) and the *Yamabiko* ones (orange).

Centre: The initial pocket timetable for the Tohoku Shinkansen when it opened in June 1984.

Below: A Series 200 emerges from a tunnel on the Tohoku Shinkansen near Kuroiso, north of Utsunomiya.   *Mikio Miura*

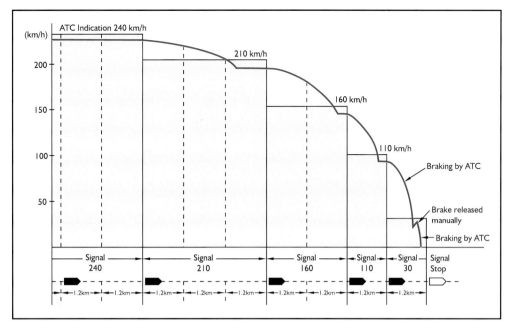

ATC braking control for the Tohoku and Joetsu Shinkansen after the maximum speed had been raised to 240 km/h (149 m.p.h.) in 1983.

West Coast Class 86s and 87s. As the lines were built entirely in the area served by the 50 Hz Grid, the trains operate on this frequency.

Two other electrical supply changes made when the Sanyo Line was built were continued on the two northern routes. The first involved the provision of a much heavier compound-catenary system for the overhead wiring to withstand the passage of many pantographs. The second change involved the system used for the return current to reach the feeder station. (If this manages to find a way of leaking to earth, interference and corrosion can take place with nearby buried underground service pipes and cables). Originally the Tokaido Line had booster transformers to step up the return current from the trains, as used almost universally on ac electrified lines in the UK. The Sanyo adopted the so-called 2 x 25 kV system, which has a separate high voltage feeder suspended from insulators on the overhead supports. At intervals this is connected to the rails and the catenary system by auto-transformers. These boost the traction supply, as well as providing the path for the return current to the much larger auto-transformer in the feeder station. In France the TGVs use this system, and it is likely to be adopted for the Channel Tunnel Rail Link.

Rolling Stock Fleet

The Series 0 trains on the Tokaido and Sanyo Shinkansen underwent some modifications during their earlier years, and train formations were changed from time to time. However, prior to 'Privatisation' in 1987, it was this type of stock, substantially unchanged from an engineering point of view, which was used for the vast majority of the services on those lines. (The first of the Series 100 sets started operating on the Tokaido Line in 1985, but it was not until the following year that mass-production began, so the description of these units is being left until Chapter 8).

The situation on the Tohoku and Joetsu Lines was different, however, with three separate 'Fleets' being used between 1980, when the first trains were delivered, and 'Privatisation' in 1987. The initial sets were of the E-fleet type, and consisted of 12 cars, all fully motored. From the passengers' point of view they included one Green Car, and an ordinary car which was also provided with a buffet. Table 6.4 shows how the E-fleet built up from 1980 to 1982 to a maximum of 36 sets. After the initial delivery of nine sets in 1980 for trial running and service on the Tohoku

Line, a further six were constructed in the following year, ready for the commencement of commercial services on both lines from November 1982. As traffic built up, a final five sets were provided in 1982. The E-fleet had then reached its maximum of 36 sets, with a total of 432 cars.

In 1983 it proved possible to increase the maximum speed on the Tohoku and Joetsu Shinkansen to 240 km/h (149 m.p.h.), thanks to the noise-suppression measures taken during its construction. Accordingly three new F-fleet sets were purchased, which were geared for the higher speed, and also included two other significant electrical modifications. Covers were constructed round the pantographs, and the number of them was reduced. It will be recalled that one of the problems with the UK Advanced Passenger Train (APT) was that its two power cars had to be marshalled together in the centre of the train so they could share a pantograph. If they had been at the outer ends of the train, travelling waves would have been set up in the overhead contact-wire which would have caused the pantographs to bounce clear of it, with loss of power and potential damage.

The French TGVs got round the trouble by using a roof-mounted 25 kV power-line, an arrangement that was not then acceptable to the UK Railway Inspectorate, but the

One of the magnificent embroideries in the royal waiting rooms at Tokyo Central station, showing Mount Fuji in cherry-blossom time. The central panel is nearly 4 feet by 5 feet in size.

safety-conscious JNR did not see it as a danger either. So, as the speeds went up, JR reduced the number of Shinkansen pantographs from the original one on every alternate coach, and connected the power supplies for the whole train with a roof-line at full catenary voltage. This had two other advantages, as noise and sparking were both reduced. During his 1982 visit to Japan, the author stayed in a hotel room which overlooked the Sanyo Shinkansen, and on a clear night it was possible to monitor the progress of departing trains for some five miles from the continuous flicker caused by their pantographs. An electrical connection between two pantographs (or pick-up shoes) reduces the current being interrupted when one of them leaves the supply system, so making the flash correspondingly smaller.

The F-fleet was expanded by a further 19 12-car sets in 1984 for the increased services which began with the extension to Ueno, and another two were added the following year, by which time there were 57 sets in all, comprising 684 cars. Changes of a totally different sort started to take place the following year when some of the E-fleet were converted to the G-fleet by shortening their formations. To start the process off, four new driving cars were built and these had the more pointed profile adopted for the Series 100 sets on the Tokaido Line. While clearly belonging to the same 'Bullet-Nose' family, their design was much 'sharper', in line with contemporary styling, while the headlights became horizontal slits rather than ovals. Initially the G-fleet formations consisted of 10 cars, and bar/buffet facilities were discontinued. They were used for the 'all-stations' *Aoba* and *Toki* services. Using the four new driving cars, and the other cars released by shortening ten of the existing E-fleet sets, it was possible to produce an additional pair of F-fleet sets, as well as the 10 new G-fleet ones.

In 1987 eight of the G-fleet sets were shortened to eight cars, and the full-length Green Car altered to a 'Composite' layout (to use the long-standing UK terminology). The remaining pair of G-fleet sets were converted into four more F-fleet ones, by providing two intermediate cars with driving cabs, and utilising other displaced cars. These complicated changes were needed to match resources with demand without buying new trains, at a time when money for investment was limited, because the JNR deficit was rising exponentially. Long-distance travel on the Tohoku and Joetsu Shinkansen was rising at this time by 8–13% annually, but numbers using the all-stations *Aoba* and *Toki* services were falling. We will see how these two routes fared after 'Privatisation' later in the book.

Train Services, Speeds and Passengers

Table 6.5 shows how the basic number of trains operated on the Tohoku and Joetsu Shinkansen changed between the start of services in 1982 and 1987, when JNR was privatised. It will be seen that the longer route to Morioka was the busier throughout, but neither matched the two older Shinkansen, for which the corresponding figures are given in Table 5.2. The cut-back in the all-station *Toki* workings in 1986, following the fall-off in passengers using them, is clearly marked.

As with the comparable figures for the Tokaido and Sanyo Shinkansen quoted earlier, the information in Table 6.5 refers to the daily numbers of trains regularly scheduled, but various additional workings also took place. Notable among these was the Imperial Special run on 29 June 1982 to take Emperor Hirohito from Omiya to Nasu-Shiobara.

	Tohoku Shinkansen			Joetsu Shinkansen			Grand
Year	Yamabiko	Aoba	Total	Asahi	Toki	Total	Total
1982							
June	8	12	20	–	–	–	20
November	36	24	60	22	20	42	102
1985							
March	58	36	94	34	34	68	162
1986							
November	58	36	94	34	31	65	161

Table 6.5
Tohoku & Joetsu Shinkansen Train Serives 1982–1986
(Basic numbers of trains per day)

Source: JNR

As this could not start from Tokyo Central station, the Emperor would not have been able to use the splendid imperial suite and passageway hidden below the platforms there. From the entrance-door at the end of the avenue from the palace, the marble-floored and walled route crosses the full width of the station to reach the Tokaido Line platforms on the far side.

The Emperor had first travelled on the Tokaido Shinkansen back in 1965, and when one of the imperial journey begins, the Stationmaster, after receiving the Emperor, walks before him to the platform concerned. He has to keep the correct distance ahead, regardless of how fast the imperial personage walks, so strategically-placed staff line the corridor and signal unobtrusively to the stationmaster whether to speed up or slow down. The author was privileged to see the imperial waiting room in 1982, with its separate thrones for the Emperor and Empress, which, however, they rarely use. This is because the railway would never normally consider making the imperial party wait before getting on their train.

On a more prosaic level, during the first year the new Shinkansen were in operation, 28 extra trains were run daily on the Tohoku Line during the summer, while there were up to 12 additional workings daily over the New Year holiday period. In all, 26 765 trains ran on the Tohoku Line between the opening in June 1982 and 14 November 1983. The Joetsu Line, which serves several skiing resorts, had up to 10 extra trains a day during the New Year holidays and winter-sports season, giving a total of 15 795 in its first year. So popular were the new services that there was at times considerable overcrowding, one *Yamabiko* on 17 August 1982 loading to 312% of capacity! Between June and November that year the loadings on the *Yamabiko* as a whole averaged 115%, while the stopping *Aoba* were somewhat less full with a figure of only 106%. These figures fell off considerably once the more frequent services began in the November. Both lines produced an increase of 17% in passengers during their first year of operation compared with the numbers previously using the corresponding 'Japanese-gauge' lines.

As always on JNR, comprehensive figures were kept of the causes of any delay, which were remarkably small during the first operating year for these two new lines. On the Tohoku there were 47 incidents, compared with 30 on the Joetsu, which is not high by any standard. A lot of lessons had been learnt since the start-up of the Tokaido Line, when the corresponding total was 372. There was only one delay on the Joetsu which was categorised as a 'Train Accident', but this was no more serious than the overheating of the resistors after a blower contactor had failed.

This admirable achievement resulted in part from the extensive pre-service running that took place. In August 1982, when the author visited the lines' main maintenance depot at Sendai, units were already coming in for bogie changes. That site, built on ground reclaimed from paddy fields using fill from the top of a nearby hill, had a total length of 3.5 km (2.2 miles), which included a large grid of storage sidings. As at the UK Eurostar depot at North Pole, its own signal cabin was provided to control internal movements. So proud were the Sendai staff of theirs that, on entry, everyone, visitors included, replaced their outdoor shoes with slippers!

It was most impressive to stand at the side of a pit in the servicing building and watch one of the Series 200 sets run in above our heads. Equally striking were the bogie-changing facilities. Several cars were lifted simultaneously, and the old bogies were then moved out along the track using a conveyor chain, while reconditioned ones were fed in at the other end. A traverser moved the bogies sideways on to a parallel storage siding, and from this another traverser and turntable led to the stripping line. After an air-blast clean in a booth, the electric motors were removed to their own overhaul bay. In no time at all, first the bogie itself, and then the wheelsets, were stripped to their components for appropriate attention, so nothing was left on the rails!

For the 1982–1987 period, the changes in journey times from Ueno are shown in Table 6.6. It will be seen that, over the shorter distances, the time savings initially were not all that great, because of the change needed to or from the 'Relay' at Omiya. To Utsunomiya there was initially a saving of 12 minutes, but this jumped to 38 once there were through workings from Ueno and the running speed had gone up from 210 to 240 km/h. Over the longest journey to Morioka, the saving was 2hr 27 min to begin with, and this came down by a further 1hr 11 min once 240 km/h running was permitted and Ueno had become the railhead.

In the *Railway Gazette International's* two-yearly speed surveys, the Tohoku and Joetsu Shinkansen did not appear until after the 1984 speed-up. Tables 6.7 and 6.8 give the 1985 figures for the fastest start-to-stop speed and the fastest overall speeds, inclusive of intermediate stops. Prior to this the Tokaido and Sanyo Shinkansen took pride of place in Japan, but in the 1985 start-to-stop list, *Yamabiko* were responsible for the first 70 runs in the table, followed by two *Asahi* from Nagaoka to Omiya which averaged 183.3 km/h (113.8 m.p.h.) over the 213.8km (132.8 miles).

Table 6.6
Journey Times from Ueno on Tohoku and Joetsu Shinkansen Routes

	Before Shinkansen (1981)	Relay Train via Omiya (June 1982)	From Ueno direct (March 1985)
Tohoku Shinkansen to:			
Utsunomiya	1hr 22min	1hr 10min	44min
Fukushima	3hr 16min	2hr 8min	1hr 27min
Sendai	4hr 14min	2hr 38min	1hr 53min
Morioka	6hr 23min	3hr 56min	2hr 45min
Joetsu Shinkansen to:			
Takasaki	1hr 16min	1hr 15min	46min
Nagaoka	3hr 18min	2hr 7min	1hr 31min
Niigata	4hr 11min	2hr 31min	1hr 53min

Source: JNR Timetables

Only then did the first pair of *Hikari* appear, with their average of 181.1 km/h (112.5 m.p.h.) between Hiroshima and Okayama.

Table 6.9 shows the annual passenger-kilometres for the two new Shinkansen between 1982 and Privatisation in 1987. Throughout, the Tohoku Line was achieving more than double the Joetsu's figure, but, even so, the 8.5 billion for 1987 should be compared with the corresponding figure of 44.2 billion chalked up by the Tokaido and Sanyo Shinkansen that year (see Table 5.1). Going back to the corresponding period after the Tokaido had opened, its figure had been 21.0 billion. It was clear that these new lines would not be so profitable as the first two, and that was confirmed by the revenue and expenses figures shown in Table 6.10. Inclusive of interest and depreciation, the loss for the Tohoku Line rose from ¥128 billion in its first year of operation to ¥159 billion in 1985/86, before dropping to ¥145 billion in the last year before 'Privatisation'. On the other hand, the Joetsu losses grew steadily in the five years concerned. It was clear that, when East Japan Railway assumed responsibility for these two lines in 1987, it would need to look very carefully at ways of improving their profitability.

To conclude this chapter, it is worth considering the overall economics of the four Shinkansen Lines as they were at the end of March 1987, on the eve of 'Privatisation'. Table 6.11 shows the length of each of the four lines, their building costs, and compares the costs per unit length. The cumulative profit or loss each line had achieved since opening is given in Table 6.12. Up to that time the Tokaido and Sanyo Lines had operated as an entity, so their profit figure of

Table 6.7
Fastest Tohoku and Joetsu Shinkansen Start-to-Stop Speeds

				Distance		Time	Speed	
Year	Train	From	To	km	miles	min	km/h	mph
1985	1 Yamabiko	Koriyama	Omiya	182.6	113.5	53	206.7	128.4

Source: *Railway Gazette International*

Table 6.8
Fastest Tohoku and Joetsu Shinkansen Journeys, inclusive of intermediate stops

				Distance		Time		No. of	Speed	
Year	Train	From*	To*	km	miles	hr	min	Stops	km/h	mph
1985	8 Yamabiko	Ueno	Morioka	492.9	306.3	2	45	3	179.2	111.3

* Some of the multiple journeys may be in the opposite direction.

Source: *Railway Gazette International*

Table 6.9
Tohoku & Joetsu Shinkansen Passenger-Kilometres 1982–1987

Year	Tohoku Line (billion)	Joetsu Line (billion)
1982/83*	3.7	0.9
1983/84	6.0	2.3
1984/85	6.2	2.5
1985/86	8.1	3.5
1986/87	8.2	3.4

* Lines only open for part of year.

Source: JNR

Table 6.10 Tohoku & Joetsu Shinkansen Revenue and Expenditure 1982–1987 (Billions of Yen)						
	Tohoku Shinkansen			**Joetsu Shinkansen**		
Year	Revenue	Expenses†	Profit/Loss	Revenue	Expenses†	Profit/Loss
1982/83*	84	212	-128	21	55	-34
1983/84	133	289	-156	54	143	-89
1984/85	144	302	-158	63	153	-90
1985/86	208	367	-159	82	159	-77
1986/87	206	363	-157	91	194	-103

* Lines only open for part of year.

† Including interest and depreciation.

Source: JNR

Opposite page: A series 200 near Echigo-Yuzawa in the winter snows that afflict the Tohoku Shinkansen.

Bottom: An aerial view of the Sendai Shinkansen Rolling Stock Base on the Tohoku Shinkansen. *JNR*

Table 6.11 Building costs for Shinkansen					
	Length		**Approx.Cost**	**Approx. Unit Cost**	
Line	km	Miles	¥ Billion	¥ million/km	¥ million/mile
Tokaido	515.4	320.3	380	740	1200
Sanyo	553.8	344.1	910	1650	2600
Tohoku	496.6	308.6	2800	5640	9100
Joetsu	295.5	183.6	1630	5500	8900

Source: *The Privatisation of Railways in Japan*, East Japan Railway Culture Foundation (1995), JR-E.

Table 6.12 Shinkansen Finances as at March 1987				
	Initial Length		**Cumulative Cost**	**Profit/Loss***
Line	km	Miles	(¥ billion)	(¥ billion)
Tokaido	515.4	320.3	380	4750
Sanyo	553.8	344.1	910	
Tohoku	496.6	308.6	2800	-745
Joetsu	295.5	183.6	1630	-401
TOTALS	1835.1	1156.6	5720	3604

* Including interest and depreciation.

Sources: *The Privatisation of Railways in Japan*, East Japan Railway Culture Foundation.
Japan Railway & Transport Review, October 1994, JR-E.

¥4750 billion is a combined total. While this was approximately four times their combined construction cost, it does not necessarily follow that they were equally profitable. The Tohoku and Joetsu Lines were still running heavy deficits for 1986/87, and their combined loss in that year was nearly 60% of the surplus produced by the Tokaido and Sanyo Lines. Only 65% of the total capital so far invested in the high-speed system had been recovered, and this was only being paid off at an overall rate of 10% per year.

In comparison with these Japanese figures, it is worth recording that as late as 1994 only 2406 km (1450 miles) of dedicated high-speed lines were in operation in the whole of Europe. Japan had reached a total of 1835 km (1156 miles) twelve years earlier, when the Joetsu Shinkansen began operating.

CHAPTER 7
'Privatisation'

In 1964 JNR's expenditure exceeded its revenue, and its deficit then grew rapidly, in spite of its management improvement plans. Two years later the reserves had all been utilised, and deficits were being carried forward. By 1971 the accounts were in the red even before allowance had been made for depreciation. Between then and 1980 there were four attempts by the government to deal with the problem, but the accumulated deficit continued to grow. In spite of increasing fares 11 times in the 13 years from 1974, the accumulated sum had reached ¥15 500 billion in 1986. (In places the effect of these rises made the JNR fares twice those of a private railway operating a parallel route). By the time the system was 'privatised' in April 1987, the deficit had shot up to no less than ¥25 400 billion, and was threatening to go into orbit! On top of this there was another obligation of ¥4900 billion for the pension fund, the grand total coming to more than the combined debts of Brazil and Mexico. At this time the Shinkansen system was earning about 40% of the total JNR revenue, so one can easily imagine how dire the railway's finances would have been if the high-speed lines had not been built.

One can easily see why drastic changes were necessary, but a satisfactory solution took a long time to work out. On one occasion at the National Railway Museum, the writer entertained a former JNR President, who considered he had 'failed' because he had been unable to find a solution, but it needed two Ad Hoc Commissions on Administrative Reform to come up with a way forward.

There were two main reasons for this loss-making situation, but both ultimately came back to the railway/government relationship. Although from the 1960s onwards, competition from road and air caused JNR to lose market share, railways have played a more important part in Japan's economy than in most industrial countries, particularly within its large cities. The government thus kept a tight grip on the whole JNR system. Budgets and fares were discussed in detail between the two bodies, and top managerial appointments were made by the government. There were often pressures too for expenditure to be made in a politician's own area, which JNR found it difficult to argue against. A large number of staff was also needed by JNR to handle relationships with the Ministry of Transport and the Diet.

Even more significant was the fact that negotiations with the unions were carried out by the government, rather than the railway. Consequently the attitude developed that 'the government would foot the bill', regardless of the ultimate effect on staff productivity. There were many different railway unions in Japan, and the principal ones were the most

militant in the country. Although, as public employees, JNR staff were in theory prevented from taking industrial action, there were still strikes from time to time. Industrial relations on the railways were thus unstable, discipline was lax, and morale low.

Staff numbers had fallen from 470 000 to 420 000 between 1970 and 1980, but there was a monolithic management structure which resulted in too many staff being employed in the less profitable areas. In 1982, when the writer was making an extensive tour of JNR, at one quite small station he was tactless enough to ask about the hours when it closed overnight, not realising it remained open 'round the clock'. The nation-wide standardisation also resulted in fare-levels being inflexible, and it could be difficult to tailor train services to meet local requirements. At the same time the accounting system prevented a proper managerial awareness of costs and profits, as a result of cross-subsidization.

Another serious handicap was the fact that JNR was only allowed to run railways, and could not become involved in any other commercial activity. In the early 1980s there was a proposal to build a large tower-block above the main JNR station in Osaka, the country's second commercial centre, and very special arrangements had to be worked out to enable this to be done legally. A block or two away, however, was the underground terminus of the private Hanshin Railway, with its Hanshin Department Store situated above it. That company operated a frequent electric service to Kobe, where another railway-owned building was situated above the station there. In addition, half way between the two cities was the Hankyu Baseball Stadium, with its own station alongside!

The Japanese private railway companies have steadily diversified and, overall, their revenue from non-railway business is now tending to equal that from the original activity they were set up to carry out. The most extreme example is the Tokyu company whose railway activities in the Tokyo area only produce 7% of its total income. Against this sort of background it is not surprising that between 1974 and 1986 JNR's passenger-kilometres fell by 8%, while those for the long-established private railways rose by just over a quarter.

The solution finally adopted was to split JNR into six regional passenger railways, with a nationwide freight company having running powers over these companies' tracks, for which they only paid the avoidable costs. Although this provides something akin to the UK Railtrack situation for the freight company, the basic idea of splitting infrastructure from train-operating was not entertained. The seven companies were each given a private-sector constitution, but initially the government held all their shares. In addition to these operating companies, a number of other bodies was set up, the most significant for our story being the Shinkansen Holding Corporation (SHC) and the Japanese National Railways Settlement Corporation (JNRSC). Both of these were state-owned.

The names of the operating companies are given in the box, which includes the initials customarily used in the UK to refer to them. They jointly still utilise the initials JR, which was determined in February 1987, and appear in each company's house colour on items as diverse as stationery and rolling-stock.

Japanese Railway Companies after Privatisation			
Name	Abbreviation	Initials used in UK	House Colour
East Japan Railway	JR East	JR-E	Green
Central Japan Railway	JR Central or JR Tokai	JR-C	Orange
West Japan Railway	JR West	JR-W	Blue
Hokkaido Railway	JR Hokkaido	JR-H	Light green
Shikoku Railway	JR Shikoku	JR-S	Light blue
Kyushu Railway	JR Kyushu	JR-K	Red
Japan Freight Railway	JR Freight	JR-F	Deep blue

Table 7.1 Operating Statistics of Privatised Railway Companies (April 1987)					
Company	Route km	Passenger-km (billion)	Staff	Assets (¥ billion)	Long-term Debt (¥ billion)
JR East	7 657	104.5	82 469	3 884.5	3 298.7
JR Central	2 003	41.1	21 410	552.9	319.1
JR West	5 325	45.8	51 538	1 316.3	1 015.8
JR Hokkaido	3 176	3.9	12 719	976.1	–
JR Shikoku	880	1.7	4 455	323.9	
JR Kyushu	2 406	7.7	14 589	738.0	–
TOTALS	**21447**	**204.7**	**187 180**	**7 791.7**	**4 633.6**

	Operating km	Tonne-km (billion)	Staff	Assets (¥ billion)	Long-term Debt (¥ billion)
JR Freight	10 010	20.0	12 005	163.7	94.4
TOTAL JR			**199 185**	**7 955.4**	**4 728.0**

Source: *The Privatisation of Railways in Japan*, East Japan Railway Culture Foundation (1985).

The six passenger companies were in two very different leagues from the size point of view. On the main island of Honshu the JNR system was split into three extremely large companies, with the network divided into self-contained, eastern, central and western sections. The other companies were much smaller, and each took over the JNR lines on the three other large islands, Hokkaido, Shikoku and Kyushu. Table 7.1 summarises the vital statistics for each of the seven companies. The aim of this division was to enable each of the passenger railways to tailor its services to the requirements of its own region.

There were, in consequence, considerable differences between the companies, particularly between the three big Honshu ones and the rest. The split and the finances were intended to give each company the possibility of earning pre-tax profits of more than 1% of turnover, and dividends of approximately 5% on the capital after five years. It was considered that the three Honshu companies and JR Freight could do this as well as taking over a share of the outstanding long-term debts, but these only equalled a small proportion of the former JNR total. On the other hand, the three smaller passenger companies were not expected to be able to meet the profitability targets themselves, so Stabilisation Funds were set up for each of them, the interest from which provided a subsidy.

These statistics do not, however, tell quite the whole story, as the expensive infrastructure of the four Shinkansen routes did not pass to these railway companies, but was held collectively by the state-owned Shinkansen Holding Corporation (SHC), which leased them to the three large Honshu companies. JR-East operated the Tohoku and Joetsu Lines, JR-Central the original Tokaido Line, and JR-West the Sanyo Line. There was an important difference between this set-up and the UK Railtrack/Train Operating Company arrangements, as the Japanese companies only paid a basic 'rights' fee to SHC, and had to carry out all infrastructure maintenance and improvements themselves. This set-up needed changing within a few years for reasons that will be discussed later.

Although JNR staff numbers had declined from 420 000 in 1980 to 277 000 by the beginning of the financial year 1986/87, this total was far more than the separate companies needed. Detailed studies enabled the most effective manning level to be worked out, and the companies were obliged to take on 20% more staff than this, so a total of 205 586 continued to be employed, including those working in the Settlement Corporation (JNRSC). This left a surplus of just under 74 000, and their problems were handled in a number of different ways, which can be summarised in Table 7.2, the figures being given to the nearest thousand.

A fundamental change in railway employment culture took place during this time, as promotions ceased to be made automatically on education attainments and seniority. Instead formal testing systems were introduced to evaluate each employee's abilities and motivation. Productivity increased as a result. On an overall revenue basis the productivity figure for the JR Group rose by 42% in five years, but JR Freight's ton-kilometres increased by 44% in just three. The other companies achieved a 45% increase in passenger-kilometres over the whole of this period. During the five years leading up to Privatisation JNR's passenger-kilometres had only averaged an annual increase of 0.6%, while JNR's freight operations lost an annual average of 9.5% of its tonne-kilometres during its final five years.

Overall the 1987–91 period saw rapid growth in Japan's economy, its Gross Domestic Product rising annually by as much as 7.5%. That peak was in 1990, but two years later the increase had fallen to under 1%. Even so there was still a rising trend in the number of 'domestic tourism' journeys being made, as the population became more affluent and their average age increased. The 'Privatised' JR passenger railways were well poised to take advantage of this.

Table 7.2 Redeployment of Surplus JNR staff	
Voluntary retirement	39 000
Ordinary retirement	6 000
Transfer to public sector	19 000
Laid off, preliminary to retirement	2 000
Taken over by JNRSC for retraining etc	8 000
TOTAL	74 000

The final group became the responsibility of the JNRSC for the next three years, during which they received vocational training and guidance, which covered an extremely wide field of occupations.

The cost of this scheme came to more than £3 billion (¥ 700 billion). By April 1990 the position of the 6,580 of the former JNR employees was as follows:

Re-employed by JR	2 300
Found jobs outside JR	3 440
Resigned from JNRSC system	840
TOTAL	6 580

This left just 1,050 who had refused all the alternative jobs they had been offered, and they were then discharged.

In the years that followed Privatisation, the numbers employed in the railway business fell appreciably, as shown by the following figures:

Year	Total employees ('000)
1987	180
1988	170
1989	164
1990	159
1991	158
1992	158

The massive container section of the JNR freight terminal in Tokyo in 1966. A Tokaido Shinkansen crosses the viaduct in the background.

JNR

We must now return to 1987 to consider how the vast JNR debts and liabilities were handled. They totalled ¥37 100 billion, which at the current rate of exchange equalled roughly £125 billion. The details of its make-up are given in Table 7.3.

It was up to the new private JR companies to deal with their own debts, and, as originally laid down, the leasing payments for the Shinkansen tracks would extinguish the Holding Corporation's debt by the end of 30 years. However, that still left two-thirds of the total to be recovered by the Settlement Corporation by other means.

JNR had owned a lot of redundant railway land, particularly former freight facilities, some of which was sited in areas of large cities where ground-space was at a premium. As had happened with the British Rail Property Board, any non-operational railway land was handed over to the JNR Settlement Corporation for ultimate disposal, and it was estimated they would realise ¥7700 billion from its sale. Another important off-set was the ¥1200 billion expected from selling the shares of the seven operating companies. In the event, both forms of redemption were much slower than originally expected. The sums in each case were extremely large, so the sales of shares, as well as land, had to be carried out gradually to avoid swamping their respective markets, which would have caused catastrophic financial losses for everyone. On the other hand, the prices paid for the shares so far sold are considerably higher than their face value, which was the figure assumed in the original calculations.

Table 7.3
Long-term Outstanding JNR Liabilities – March 1987

	¥ billion
Long-term JNR liabilities	
Assets of JR Group companies	4 700
Tokaido, Sanyo and Tohoku Shinkansen assets	3 900
Miscellaneous	16 400
TOTAL	25 000
JR Construction Public Corporation liabilities	
Existing lines in Honshu	1 200
Joetsu Shinkansen	1 800
Seikan Tunnel and other facilities	1 500
TOTAL	4 500
Other liabilities	
Pension obligations, etc	5 000
Management stabilisation funds	1 300
Honshu-Shikoku Bridge liabilities	700
Retraining, etc	700
TOTAL	7 700

Immediately after Privatisation took place in April 1987, responsibility for this total debt was shared as follows:

	¥ billion
JNR Settlement Corporation	25 600
Shinkansen Holding Corporation	5 700
JR Companies	5 900
TOTAL	**37 200**

All these disposals were originally expected to leave a residue of ¥13 800 billion, which would have had to be picked up, ultimately, by the tax-payers. It was estimated that this represented the equivalent of ¥114 313 for each Japanese citizen, or about GBP500 at the then rate of exchange.

The original proposals for dealing with the Shinkansen tracks did not work out. The system's liabilities were ¥8500 billion, but, as we have seen, the construction costs of the different lines varied enormously, as did the numbers of passengers they handled. Accordingly a formula was worked out to allocate the leasing charges to the three Honshu passenger companies on the basis of replacement value and traffic volume. Although the SHC owned the infrastructure, there was a significant difference in its relationship with the operating companies compared with the present situation in the UK. In Japan the three Shinkansen *operators* were themselves responsible for the maintenance and improvement to the infrastructure, and it proved difficult to fund these activities for an asset the companies did not own. In addition it was not clear exactly what would happen at the end of the 30-year leasing period when the infrastructure passed to the operating companies. Would it be a free transfer, or would some residual payment be demanded? This clearly had a significant bearing on the price at which the operating companies' shares could be floated on the country's stock exchanges. Accordingly it was decided to sell the Shinkansen tracks to the operators.

By October 1991, when the transfer took place, the leasing payments already made had reduced the original ¥8500 billion value of the Shinkansen by ¥500 billion, but the selling price was increased to ¥9176.7 billion. The extra ¥1100 billion was placed with the state-owned Railway Development Fund, to be used for future extensions of the high-speed network.

The sale of the Shinkansen Lines was split as shown in Table 7.4. It seems somewhat unfair that

Below: Typical Japanese-gauge EMU used for Super-Express services at the time of Privatisation.

the Tokaido Line, which had been the most economical to build, should have the highest price-tag, but it was the only one which was generating sufficient revenue to enable the whole of the network to be disposed of in a way that made economic sense for its future owners.

Since privatisation the overall operating profits of the six passenger railways have increased significantly, as Table 7.5 shows. However, it is only the three Honshu companies that are profitable, the performances of the 'island' companies providing yet another example of the worldwide difficulty of operating regional railway services in the age of the motor car. Even so they reduced their operating losses by some 10%, and their overall profitability is ensured by the interest from their Stabilisation Funds. The recent fall in interest rates, however, has prompted some observers to wonder if these funds will continue to provide a large enough subsidy.

It will also be noted that JR-East is by far the largest of the Honshu companies, as a result of its heavy involvement in handling the traffic in the Tokyo area. In the 1991 international league of companies, its sales revenues came just above Michelin's, but its passenger-kilometres exceeded those for western Germany (DB) and France put together.

By the 1990s the railway companies' freedom to become involved in other businesses had already seen the percentage of their overall income from these new activities rise from under 1% in 1987 to 3.3% in 1993. Many of these projects take a considerable time to come to fruition,

Table 7.4
Shinkansen Purchase Prices (October 1991)

Company	Lines Purchased	Apportionment Ratio (%)	Transfer Price (¥ billion)	Original Cost ¥ billion
JR East	Tohoku, Joetsu	33.857	3 106.9	4 430
JR Central	Tokaido	55.528	5 095.6	380
JR West	Sanyo	10.615	974.1	910
TOTALS			9 176.7	5 720

Source: *The Privatisation of Railways in Japan*, East Japan Railway Culture Foundation (1985).

Table 7.5 Operating Profits of JR Companies after Privatisation (¥billion)					
			Year		
Company	**1987**	**1988**	**1989**	**1990**	**1991**
JR East	248.4	259.9	256.3	262.6	265.6
JR Central	26.4	31.7	36.4	47.6	51.6
JR West	80.5	91.5	91.6	96.1	101.7
Sub Total	355.3	383.1	384.3	406.3	418.9
JR Hokkaido	− 49.5	− 48.3	− 47.8	− 46.9	− 46.9
JR Shikoku	− 14.8	− 14.4	− 14.5	− 14.0	− 14.0
JR Kyushu	− 27.0	− 25.3	− 24.6	− 23.0	− 21.8
Sub Total	− 191.3	− 88.0	− 86.9	− 83.9	− 82.7
Passenger Total	264.0	295.1	297.4	322.4	337.1
JR Freight	8.2	9.1	7.9	10.1	10.0
Grand Total	272.2	304.2	305.3	332.5	347.1

Source: *The Privatisation of Railways in Japan*, East Japan Railway Culture Foundation.

one example being 'JR-Central Towers', constructed alongside the station at Nagoya, which was not completed until 20 December 1999 . It is an enormous complex, from which two towers, housing a hotel and offices, rise to a height of over 750 feet. Until all the shares of a company have been floated on the stock exchanges, the Ministry of Transport is kept informed of all such activities. In most other matters the companies are now their own masters, with the government being at arm's length as the railway shares are held by the Settlement Corporation.

Clearly the sale of each company's shares could not take place until certain financial conditions had been met, and all three Honshu companies had achieved this position by 1992. Market conditions, however, prevented the first flotation taking place until October 1993, when 2.5 million of JR East's 4.0 million shares were released. As is customary in the UK, the selling price for a share is considerably more than its nominal value, a typical example being Railtrack, where ordinary members of the public paid a total of £3.80 for each 25p share. The JR East shares had a nominal value of ¥50 000, but they were floated at ¥380 000. This is only half the premium that Railtrack obtained, but the idea of a single share being worth more than £2000 is very strange by UK practice. By August 1996, the JR East share price has risen to no less than ¥552 000 – not a bad gain in less than three years. Another significant difference between the Japanese and UK privatisations is that there is no Rail Regulator in Japan.

At the end of 1999 the shares of the three main JR companies were held as follows:

Date	*Shares sold on stock market*	*Shares held by JR Construction Public Corporation*
JR-East		
October 1993	2 500 000	
August 1999	1 000 000	500 000
JR-Central		
October 1997	1 353 929	886 071
JR-West		
October 1996	1 365 656	634 344

LINKING JAPAN'S ISLANDS BY RAIL
The Seikan Tunnel and the Seto-Ohashi Bridges

Japan consists of four main islands, with Honshu being the central one and by far the largest. In 1942 a single-track rail tunnel was constructed under the Kanmon Strait, off the south-west end of Honshu, to link up with Kyushu, and a second parallel one was opened two years later. As recounted in Chapter 5, a twin-track Shinkansen tunnel was built in 1975, after a road tunnel and suspension bridge had been opened in 1958 and 1973, respectively.

It was not, however, until 1988 that any fixed links were completed between Honshu and the other two main islands of Hokkaido and Shikoku. The former consists of a twin-track rail tunnel, while the latter is a series of combined rail and road bridges of considerable complexity. Both these rail links could, in theory, one day become part of the Shinkansen system. It is thus appropriate to describe these two major civil engineering works, which contributed to the capital expenses incurred by JNR prior to Privatisation.

The Seikan Tunnel

The Seikan Tunnel is the longest tunnel in the world which passes under the sea. Its 53.85 km (33.5 mile) length exceeds that of the Channel Tunnel by 3.4 km (2.1 miles), but the fixed link across the English Channel has a greater length under water – 37.93 km (23.6 miles) against 23.30 km (14.5 miles). In the past, Hokkaido has been to some extent the Japanese equivalent of the American West, as people moved there to open up new land and its mineral resources. Shipping services provided the connection with Honshu across a stormy stretch of sea, which was crossed by various ferries, including some carrying railway carriages and wagons. In 1954 the *Toya-Maru*, a train-ferry sailing between Aomori and Hakodate, sank in a severe typhoon, with the loss of all but 159 of the 1314 passengers aboard. This tragic disaster prompted the idea of a tunnel, and construction began in 1964. The task was extremely difficult, and it was not until 1988 that it was opened.

The tunnel was originally intended to form part of the Shinkansen line from Tokyo to Sapporo, the main city on Hokkaido, but, as we have already seen, that had been cut back to Morioka, leaving a gap of over 150 miles between there and the tunnel's southern portal. Like all the Shinkansen tunnels, the Seikan consists of just a single bore, able to accommodate twin standard-gauge tracks, and rolling-stock of Shinkansen loading-gauge. It is thus different from the Channel Tunnel, which has separate bores for each track, with a Service Tunnel running between them for most of the distance. With the Seikan Tunnel, a separate Service Tunnel has been constructed to one side of the undersea section only, and connections between the two are at intervals of 600 metres, which makes them much less frequent than the corresponding cross-passages along the whole length of the Channel Tunnel.

There is also a Pilot Tunnel, sloping gently downwards from the centre of the Rail Tunnel to finish under each coast, which is now used for drainage purposes. At each of its ends there are inclined shafts to the surface, and there are vertical ventilation ones from the ends of the Service Tunnel. An underground station was constructed at each of the latter points, with a large hall behind the platforms. These were initially used for tourist exhibitions, but when the Shinkansen tracks are laid they will house the civil engineering depots. There are two more inclined shafts on each of the under-land sections.

Constructing the whole tunnel was an immense task because of the difficult geological conditions. The work spanned more than 20 years, having started officially in 1964. It was opened for Japanese-gauge trains in 1988. As shown in Table 7.3, the Japanese Railways Construction Public Corporation had amassed liabilities of ¥ 1500 billion in connection with the tunnel by the time of Privatisation in 1987. It will be many years before the Shinkansen tracks reach the southern portal, but, as described in Chapter 9, it will be possible to accommodate the high-speed trains as well as the existing ones by the use of mixed-gauge tracks.

There is now an extensive daily service of passenger and freight trains through the tunnel, the year-round passenger services being shown in English-language visitors' JR timetable.

The Seto-Ohashi Bridges

A very different method was used to connect Honshu with Shikoku across the Seto Inland Sea. Between Kojima at the north and Sakaide on Shikoku there is a string of islands which has linked up by a number of separate bridges, each of which carries road traffic on the upper level and rail tracks on the lower. Currently only the Japanese-gauge rails have been laid, but there is provision for Standard-gauge ones as well if the Shinkansen is extended to Shikoku.

In order from north to south there are the following bridges:

Name	Type	Total Length (metres/yards)	Main Span (metres/yards)	Tower Height (metres/feet)
Shimotsui-Seto	Suspension	1400/1531	940/1028	149/489
Hitsuishi-jima	Cable-stayed	790/ 864	790/ 864	152/499
Iwakuro-jima	Cable-stayed	790/ 864	420/ 459	161/528
Yoshima	Truss	850/ 930	245/ 268	–
Kita Bisan-Seto	Suspension	1538/1682	990/1083	184/604
Minami Bisan-Seto	Suspension	1648/1802	1100/1203	194/636

The cable-stayed Hitsuishi-jima and Iwakuro-jima Bridges join on the small island after which the latter is named, but the two Bisan-Seto suspension bridges meet at a central cable anchorage. This was constructed from more than 100 000m³ of reinforced concrete based on a carefully prepared section of the sea floor.

At the north end of the link there are the twin Washuzan Tunnels, the upper road one being 205 metres long, while the rail tracks thread a 254-metre bore. These lead on to the first suspension bridge, which is connected to the various other bridges with twin-level viaducts constructed from reinforced-concrete. *In toto* the link stretches for no less than 13 km (8 miles), forming part of the 32 km (19.9 miles) of the Seto-Chuo Expressway constructed by the Honshu-Shikoku Bridge Authority (HSBA).

The first-ever suspension bridge to carry a railway track was the one built across the River Tees when the Stockton & Darlington Railway was being extended to Middlesbrough in 1830. It was not a success, and was irrevocably strained fairly soon after it came into service. One driver was traditionally said not to have trusted its strength, and set the controls of his locomotive, before alighting to *walk* across it, while the train followed at its own speed! It may have been the Tees Bridge which discouraged engineers from employing the suspension design for railway use, as relatively few have been built in the past. The recent British-designed 1.35-mile Tsing Ma Bridge, forming part of the connection with the new Hong Kong airport, is the largest such combined structure in the world. That, however, will only have to carry the electric multiple-units serving the airport, whereas the Seto-Ohashi Bridge had to be designed for freight trains weighing no less than 1,400 tonnes as well as electric passenger services running at 120km/h (75mph). The structure successfully withstood the Great Hanshin Earthquake in January 1995.

The railways are responsible for 45% of the construction cost of this link, and, as with the Seikan Tunnel, the JNR accounts showed a liability of ¥700 billion from the Seto-Shikoku Bridge at the time of Privatisation. Soon after opening, trains across the link had attracted some 30 000 passengers/day, with about 2,500 of them being commuters. Frequent services from Okayama to destinations in east and west Shikoku use the bridge.

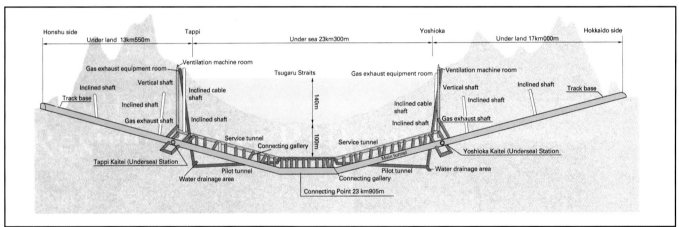

Above: Interior of Seto bridge showing railway tracks at lower level. *Mikio Miura*

Facing Page Top: The Seto–Ohashi Bridges, looking south from the north tower of the Shimotsui-Seto suspension bridge. To the left of the further tower can be seen the stayed Hitsuishi-jima and Iwakuro-jima bridges, with the final Minami Bisan-Seto suspension bridge in the far right distance. The railway tracks are on the level below the roadways.

Honshu-Shikoku Bridge Authority

Facing Page Centre: Cross-section of Seikan Tunnel showing Shinkansen and Japanese-gauge rolling stock. *JR-Hokkaido*

Facing Page Bottom: Limited Express *Hatsukari* ('Wild Goose') emerging from the southern portal of Seikan Tunnel. This is the longest tunnel in the world passing under the sea, and connects Hokkaido with Honshu.

Japan Railway Construction Public Corporation

Below: A 1966 view of the JNR train ferries which used to operate between Honshu and Hokkaido. *JNR*

CHAPTER 8

Development of the Tokaido and Sanyo Shinkansen

Although the Tokaido and Sanyo Shinkansen were leased and operated by two different railway companies from April 1987, and actually owned by them after October 1991, there remains a strong bond between them because of the considerable number of through trains operated east and west of Shin-Osaka, where crew changes take place. It is therefore logical to discuss the early years of post-Privatisation development of traffic on the two lines in the same chapter.

It is important, however, to appreciate the differences in scale between the railway operations of the two separate companies. In the first year of Privatisation, (1987/88), the Tokaido Shinkansen handled 32.1 million passenger-kilometres, whereas JR-West achieved 13.2 on their high-speed route, which was fractionally longer – (553.8 km (344.1 miles) compared with 515.4 km (320.3 miles). On the other hand, JR-West operated 4425.1 km (2 749.6 miles) of Japanese-gauge routes, whereas the corresponding figure for JR-Central was 1430.9 km (889.1 miles), so the details of their respective railway businesses differ quite appreciably.

Another significant indication of the differences in the traffic east and west of Osaka was provided in October 1991, when JR-Central had to pay more than ¥ 5000 billion for the Tokaido Shinkansen infrastructure, whereas JR-West got the slightly-longer Sanyo one for just under ¥ 1000 billion, as shown in Table 7.4. The Sanyo Shinkansen had originally cost more to build, but traffic levels were also taken into account when the purchase prices were fixed.

The 'Tokyo effect' undoubtedly has a large influence on the passenger loadings on the combined Shinkansen, in the same way as UK Intercity trains carry more passengers the nearer they get to London. An interesting analysis of the East Coast route's traffic was given to a special meeting of the Stephenson Locomotive Society marking the centenary of York station in 1977. On the eve of the introduction of the InterCity 125s, more than 80% of all journeys on that route had London as their origin or destination. All the station-to-station flows were analysed, and some 20 of the total were responsible for well over three-quarters of the traffic.

At the 1994 International High-Speed Railway Conference in Kyoto referred to in Chapter 4, Mr Toshiyuki Umehara, JR-West's Managing Director and Senior General Manager at their railway operations headquarters, spoke of the strong impact the Sanyo Shinkansen had had on the regional economies. Some 400 companies had opened branch offices in the Fukuoka area in anticipation of the Shinkansen's extension to Hakata in 1975, the vast majority of them coming from outside Kyushu. His figures showed that, for internal transport, the market share for rail peaked at 70% for journey times of about 5½ hours. The airlines' share at this range was only 20%, but started to rise quickly for journey times longer than this. Between them rail and air squeezed the private car out of the picture as the journey-times became longer still.

Although the population density along the Shinkansen route decreases west of Osaka, a lot of people in that part of Japan use ordinary trains to reach the high-speed route, and JR-West has taken steps to improve the inter-gauge connections. From the earliest days of the Okayama extension, tourist travel has also been important for the Sanyo Shinkansen, and in the 1990s the *Family Hikari* was introduced, a six-car Series 0 set which made two round trips daily between Shin-Osaka and Hakata during the summer period (20 July to 1 September). For the benefit of those travelling on holiday, one of the cars contained a saloon equipped with children's play facilities.

In Chapters 4 and 5 we have already looked at the building of these two Shinkansen lines, together with the development of their train services along the combined route up to the time of Privatisation. Further important train and speed developments occurred on the eve of that change, and these were more appropriately left until this chapter. Our story will therefore continue from that point.

Series 100 Sets

Until 1985 all the trains on the two routes were formed from Series 0 stock, with identical performance characteristics, although the layout of the passenger accommodation varied between the *Hikari* and *Kodama* sets. The basic design was, by then, over 20 years old, and technology had moved on considerably during this period.

In March 1985 a new-look 'Bullet Train' appeared when the first Series 100 set was unveiled. It had an obvious family resemblance to the earlier stock, but its styling was much 'sharper' and reflected the way design had changed throughout the world during this period. The front-end was even more impressive, with a higher and clean-cut cab, while the former oval marker lights were replaced by horizontal slits, adding to the impression of speed.

Further back in the train, however, there was an even more obvious change, as two of the cars were of the bi-level type, with large panoramic windows on the upper level, like the best of the North American 'Dome Cars'. A dining area occupied the upper level in one of these, and the other provided some of the train's Green Car (first class) seating. The lower level below the dining area accommo-

Motor bogie of Series 100 Shinkansen. *JR-Central*

dated a service corner, as well as the kitchen and other service equipment. In the Green Car there are several small cabins at the lower level, with seats for 1–4 passengers, who pay appropriate extra supplements for their privacy. The total number of seats was reduced by 19, giving 1153 ordinary and 168 Green Car ones, compared with 1208 and 132, respectively, for the corresponding Series 0 trains.

There were, however, many other new features which were not visible to the outside observer. The body structure was still fabricated from steel, rather than the light-alloy construction used for the Series 200s on the Tohoku and Joetsu Shinkansen, but a significant reduction in weight was achieved. One of the 16-car Series 100 sets tared only 925 tonnes compared with the 970 of a Series 0. Like the Mk III coaches on BR, the equipment on the underside was faired to reduce drag – and noise – at high speeds. The new shape also reduced the cab's drag-factor by almost 15%.

The tap-changer power controllers were replaced with thyristors, but these still supplied the power to 'classic' series-wound d.c. traction motors. There was, however, another major change, as four of the cars were trailers. These were the two bi-level ones and the end cars, whose more pointed noses made them 900 mm (nearly 3 ft) longer than the corresponding Series 0 design. Each of the powered axles along the train was driven by a 230 kW (310 h.p.) motor, so, in spite of the total number dropping from 64 to 48, the installed power was only marginally less – 11 040 compared with 11 840 kW (14 800 or 15 870 h.p.). The motors were force-cooled with separate blowers, the Series 0s having had the traditional EMU arrangement of self-ventilating motors with the fans on their main shafts. With fans inside the motors, the amount of cooling air that can be provided is limited - and varies with the train's speed – so the use of forced ventilation enables the rating of a motor to be increased, because this is limited by the maximum permissible temperature rise in its windings.

From the performance point of view, the new power system provided several major advantages. The initial acceleration went up from 1.0 to 1.6 km/h/s (0.6 to 1.0 m.p.h./sec). At the same time a higher gear-ratio between the motor and the axle improved the top end of the performance curve, so the balancing speed on level track increased from 235 to 276 km/h (146 to 171 m.p.h.). Further technical comparisons are given in Table 8.5 later in this chapter.

The different power supply system to the traction motors did not prevent rheostatic braking being used, but the 16 fewer motored axles reduced the amount of retardation that could be carried out this way without exceeding the adhesion limits. To make up for this, an unusual form of braking was provided on the unmotored axles. This used the Eddy Current System, as tried on the German InterCity Experimental, but there was an important difference. The latter train dispersed the energy into heat in the running rails, whereas on the Series 100 Shinkansen it was the discs on the axles which are subjected to the eddy currents which absorbed the kinetic energy of the train. Civil engineers have traditionally been concerned about the long-

term effect on the rails if they are used as 'heat sinks'. The system was abandoned on the production InterCity Expresses, although GEC-Alsthom considered its use for their 'New Generation' TGVs. The 'shoes' for an eddy-current disc do not actually touch it, but consist of a series of electromagnets close to its surface. These induce rapidly-varying currents in the disc as it rotates, which its electrical resistance then turns into heat. Unlike an ordinary disc brake, there is no physical contact between it and the 'shoes', and thus no wear.

The prototype Series 100 entered public service at the beginning of October 1985, after it had reached 143 m.p.h. (230 km/h) during trials on the Tokaido Shinkansen, followed by 162 m.p.h. (260 km/h) on the Sanyo. In the following June the production Series 100 trains went into public service on the Tokaido route, and on 1 November the maximum speed on the pioneering high-speed line was raised to 220 km/h (137 m.p.h.), the first change in 22 years. The Series 0s were permitted to run at the higher speed as well, but it was the new Series 100s which were used for the fastest *Hikari* workings. By the time of Privatisation in April 1987, there were seven of these train sets in use, and three more were obtained in 1988, but in the latter the dining facilities were dropped in preference to the cafeteria on the lower level, with additional Green Car seats 'upstairs'. As shown in Table 8.6, there was then a rapid increase in the number of these new sets in service, until the total number of cars reached 912 in 1992 (57 sets).

The higher speeds enabled the fastest Tokyo - Osaka journeys to drop below the 'magic' 3 hours in November 1986, with the fastest *Hikari* taking 2hr 56min until March 1990, when a further four minutes were trimmed off the schedules. (The last train from Tokyo, departing at 21.00, had a 2hr 52min schedule from November 1986, but was a one-off, being known, for obvious reasons, as the 'Cinderella Express').

Table 8.1 shows how the timings changed between 1964 and 1993, as well as giving the train pattern and the average number of trains operated per day. Until the introduction of the Series 100s, the hourly departures of *Hikari* and *Kodama* had been equal in number, but this then changed from '5H-5K' to '6H-4K' to take advantage of the faster running. In 1989 the pattern changed again to '7H-4K', to meet the traffic demand, with the daily average number of Tokaido departures reaching 251.

In due course JR-West also acquired some Series 100 sets, but these differed in having four bi-level cars in the centre of their formations, being known as Series 100N

Table 8.1
Changes in Tokaido Shinkansen Schedules 1964–1993

Starting Date	Standard Train Pattern*	Average No. of Trains/Day†	Fastest Travel Time Tokyo–Osaka	Notes
Mar. 1985	6H-4K	231	3hr 8min	
Nov. 1986	6H-4K	235	2hr 56min	Train speeds increased to 220 km/h (137 m.p.h.).
Mar. 1988	6H-4K	239	2hr 56min	Three new stations opened.
Mar. 1989	7H-4K	251	2hr 56min	To meet increased traffic demand.
Mar. 1990	7H-4K	263	2hr 52min¶	
Oct. 1991	7H-4K	278	2hr 52min	
Mar. 1992	8H-3K	288	2hr 30min	Train speeds increased to 270 km/h (168 m.p.h.).
Mar. 1993	1N-7H-3K	282	2hr 30min	Hourly Nozomi services introduced.

* H = *Hikari*, K = *Kodama* and N = *Nozomi*.
† Including seasonal trains
¶ The 'Cinderella Express', leaving Tokyo at 21.00, had a 2hr 52min schedule from November 1986.

Source: JR-C

Above: A Series 100 on the long viaduct across Lake Hamana. The bi-level cars can be seen towards the rear.   *JR-Central*

Below: A pair of Series 100s standing side-by-side to display their new features, the bi-level cars and the different nose profile.   *JR-Central*

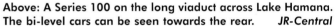

Above: Interior of a *Family Hikari* set used for summer services west of Shin-Osaka, showing children's play area. *JR-Central*

Below: Individual TV screens provided for Green Car passengers on JR-West's Series 100N *Grand Hikari*.   *JR-Central*

Facing page top: Platform departure indicators at Kyoto on a Sunday in October 1994, showing the use of western as well as Japanese lettering. It is clear that engineering work does not take place on the Shinkansen at that time on Sundays!

Right: Close-up of pantograph fences on Series 300 in Kyoto station in October 1994.

Extreme right: Series 300 driving car undergoing overhaul at Hamamatsu Workshop.   *Mikio Miura*

house-colour. Each vehicle carries its own number on the side-panelling, and the set number appears on the windscreens of the end cars.

A number of other changes had been necessary to permit the operation of the faster and more intensive services on the Tokaido Shinkansen. The original overhead electrification system had been similar to that used in the UK, with booster transformers to draw the return current out of the rails into the return cables slung from the lineside masts. The wiring also conformed to comparable standards adopted in the UK, although, by and large, this country stuck to the simple catenary system, rather than adding an intermediate wire to make it a 'compound' one.

('N' stood for 'New' Shinkansen, which might be thought of as tautology, but actually shows how the word 'Shinkansen' had become accepted as referring to the train rather than its original meaning of 'New Trunk Line'). As the bi-level cars are unmotored, a compensating change in the trains' configuration was needed to maintain the required power:weight ratio. The end cars of the Series 100N sets are accordingly provided with traction motors on each axle. One of the bi-level cars in these sets had a dining area on the upper deck, but the corresponding sections on the other three were used for Green Car passengers, with standard seating 'downstairs'. These sets were mainly used for the through *Hikari* services between Tokyo and Hakata.

In 1988 the name *West Hikari* was adopted for the faster JR-West services operating west of Shin-Osaka using Series 0 stock, and in the following March the maximum speed for the Series 100Ns on the Sanyo Shinkansen was raised to 230 km/h (143 m.p.h.), taking advantage of that line's higher design speed. These sets were primarily used for the through services to and from Tokyo, and made less stops than the other *Hikari* which were still worked by Series 0 sets. In the mid-1990s the fastest trains running between Hakata and Shin-Osaka were named *Grand Hikari*, and provided a personal video service for each Green Car passenger.

With the Series 100N sets running through east of Shin-Osaka, the number of bi-level cars in a train provided instant, long-range, identification of its ownership. With other Series it was necessary to look for the colour of the initials JR on the sides of some of the cars to determine the company to which they belonged. Sets belonging to JR-C have them in orange, while JR-W's are in that company's blue

To ensure stable current collection, the cross-section of the contact-wire was enlarged from 110 to 170 mm^2, increasing its weight by some 50%. The whole system was also tensioned more highly to improve current collection. Originally each of the three wires was stressed at 1 tonf (10kN), comparable with the BR 25 kV standard system. For 220 km/h running on the Tokaido Shinkansen, the tensions in the contact wire and auxiliary catenary were upped by 50%, while that for the main catenary was increased by a factor of 2½, to 2.5 tonf (25kN). As described in Chapter 6, at high speeds multiple pantographs on a train can cause standing-waves in the overhead wiring, which impede current collection and can cause damage. The eight pantographs per train fitted on the Series 0s were reduced to six initially on the Series 100s, and these were later cut to three, with a roof-mounted power-line connecting them, as had been done with the Series 200s on the Tohoku and Joetsu Shinkansen when their speeds were pushed up to 240 km/h.

To enable the masts to take the increased stresses, pairs of them on the opposite sides of the track had their tops connected with an arched pipe-beam. Japanese practice differs in two other respects from that in the UK, as there is a continuous protective wire (earth) slung from the outside of each mast at the top, whereas in the Uk the base of each lineside structure is earthed individually to the track. The Japanese installations also have flashover-arrestors around the end nearer the mast of each 25 kV insulator on the supporting bracket arms. These are connected to the earth wire, and prevent the current from any flashover causing damage to the concrete masts, or passing down metal ones into the ground.

The cab signalling system also had to be changed to cope with the higher speed, with additional speed bands being provided in the ATC system. Within a few years, the maximum line speed was upped further, and the ATC had to be changed again, so the details of these signalling alterations will be described later in this chapter.

During the final year of JNR, the combined traffic density on the Tokaido and Sanyo Shinkansen was 44.2 billion passenger-km, and this rose to 45.6 billion in 1987/88. As shown in Table 8.2, the figure then climbed quickly as the benefits of Privatisation and faster trains took effect, topping 50 billion by 1989. At the same time competitive forms of transport were also being improved. Faster aircraft and more regional airports cut the overall journey times by that mode, while more motorways were being opened. Although the maximum permitted speed on these is low by UK standards, and toll-booths appear quite frequently, they nevertheless presented a long-term threat to the Shinkansen.

Series 300 Sets

JR-Central accordingly put in hand plans to increase speeds on the Tokaido Shinkansen to no less than 270 km/h (168 m.p.h.), and build new trains capable of running at this speed. While the design of the Series 100s could be said to have *evolved* from that of the first 'Bullet Trains', it needed a design *revolution* to produce a train that could be permitted to run at 270 km/h. This was 50 km/h (31 m.p.h.) more than currently allowed, and 20 km/h (12 m.p.h.) faster than the original design figure for the Tokaido Shinkansen. Above all, the trains had to remain environmentally acceptable.

The first Series 300 set, as it was officially designated, was completed in March 1990, and its appearance initially caused a considerable shock. Gone was the 'Bullet Train' image, and at the front the roof-line swept smoothly down through 90° to end in a horizontal wedge at rail level, like the inverted bow of a boat. There was no prominent windscreen to provide any discontinuity, the driver's forward vision being provided by a glazed area which gave an optical illusion of pointing upwards rather than horizontally. It was matched by a narrower horizontal band across the nose, incorporating the headlights. The roof-line of the train was much lower, but the pantographs, which clearly had to reach the same height as those on the earlier designs, were surrounded by higher shields.

At high speeds pantographs present two separate problems for the railway engineer. The first results from the buffeting of the airflow sweeping over the roof of the train, which can make the pantograph bounce off the overhead contact-wire, interrupting the current collection. The second problem is the noise, which can arise in two ways. At high speeds the rods from which the pantograph is constructed create a series of vortices which are very noisy. Some years ago I realised how serious this could be when I travelled up Snaefell in the Isle of Man. At the summit the noise from the lattice radio mast and its supporting wires was deafening, even though the wind was not all that strong.

The resistance of a body passing through the air goes up as the square of the speed, so it needs a force four times larger to double the speed. That is difficult enough for the traction engineers, but the sound generated by protuberances like cabs and pantographs increases with the *fourth* to the *sixth power* of the speed. At the worst, this means that going 10% faster makes the noise 75% louder! It has therefore become customary to surround the pantographs with streamlined fences which deflect the main airflow away from them. They also intercept some of noise being radiated downwards towards the lineside. Lower versions of these had long been fitted to the Series 0 sets, significantly changing their appearance from that shown in the photographs of them in the earlier chapters.

A lot of changes were made with the pantograph arrangements on the Series 300 sets. The prototype was fitted with no less than five, but those on cars 3 and 15 were removed after running tests, and, when the trains went into regular service, they operated with only the centre and rear ones in use. From 1995 the central ones were progressively removed, leaving just the two 'end' ones as standard, which reduced the additional noise *inside* the train caused by the fences while it was travelling through tunnels. If an independent pantograph separates from the contact wire, even for a short distance, it will draw an arc, which makes a noise. Back in 1985 it was discovered that arcs of this type were prevented by installing a bus-line connecting all the pantographs on a train. The adoption of such an arrangement significantly reduced the noise by 3dB(A), which added to the improvement that had been obtained three years earlier by grinding the surface of the rails.

There were, needless to say, very good reasons for all these changes. The Tokaido Shinkansen operates through many populous areas, where noise and vibration had caused environmental complaints nearly two decades earlier, when train services were much less intensive. In effect, higher speeds could only be tolerated as long as there was no environmental deterioration, and many design changes were made with this in mind.

The cab shape of the Series 300, for example, cut the air-resistance factor by a further 20% from that of the Series 100s, which also decreased the noise generation. Another example of the micro-streamlining carried out was the replacement of the sliding passenger doors with the flush-fitting plug type. While the coach widths were not altered, the roof height was dropped from 13.1 to 12.0 feet (4.0 to 3.65 metres), although the interior ceiling height remained the same. The use of light alloys for the bodies added to the weight savings, and the weight of a 16-car set fell to 710 tonnes compared with the 925 tonnes for a Series 100. The maximum axle-load of 16.0 tonnes for a Series 0 had fallen to 15.0 for the Series 100s, but dropped to an astonishing 11.3 with the third-generation train.

	Table 8.2 Tokaido & Sanyo Shinkansen Passengers and Passenger-Kilometres			
	Tokaido Shinkansen		Sanyo Shinkansen	
Year	Passengers (million)	Passenger-km (billion)	Passengers (million)	Passenger-km (billion)
1987/88	102.1	32.1	55.0	13.2
1988/89	112.1	36.3	61.2	14.8
1989/90	117.3	37.4	62.2	15.2
1990/91	129.6	41.3	66.4	16.1
1991/92	133.9	41.8	68.5	16.3
1992/93	132.2	40.7	68.6	16.2
1993/94	131.8	40.5	67.9	16.0
1994/95	128.2	38.9	57.7	13.3
1995/96	132.8	39.8	63.5	14.8
1996/97	134.2	41.0	64.4	15.5
1997/98	134.4	41.1	62.8	15.0
1998/99	130.3	39.4	60.2	14.2

Source: JR-C, JR-W

Above: Motor bogie of Series 300 *Nozomi*. Note absence of bolster compared with illustrations of Series 0 and Series 100 designs. The light-weight gearbox can also be seen.   *JR-Central*

Above: Bolsterless trailer bogie for Series 300 *Nozomi*, showing eddy-current braking discs.   *JR-Central*

As well as taking advantage of the lower body weight possible with light-alloy construction, the power system on the Series 300s represented a major step-change. The d.c. traction motors, which had been used in both previous designs, gave way to three-phase a.c. ones, which, in Japanese parlance, are said to be driven by a 'Variable-Voltage, Variable-Frequency' (VVVF) power system. Not only are they much lighter and smaller, but have a more rugged and simpler internal design, requiring less maintenance. Table 8.3 gives some comparisons between the two motor designs. It will be seen that, compared with the Series 100, the a.c. motors are half the weight, and occupy half the space, but their maximum output is 30% greater. As a result, only 10 of the Series 300 cars need to be powered, compared with 12 on the Series 100.

The traction supply equipment for the motors on the Series 300s is shared between several adjacent cars, one having the transformer and those on either side the converters and inverters providing the variable-frequency three-phase current for its four asynchronous traction motors. As well as being simpler in design, the characteristics of these 'squirrel-cage' motors enable them to produce full power at higher rotational speeds compared with the traditional series-wound dc design, the latter requiring field-weakening equipment worked by mechanical contactors. On the Series 300s, the solid-state 'power electronics' do all necessary switching, but a complicated computer control-system is needed, and the electronic equipment needs to be cooled. Thyristors are constructed from semi-conductors which have a significant electrical resistance, which, with the current flows needed to drive the train, produce an appreciable amount of heat. In addition, the energy contained in a thyristor every time it is turned off, several hundred times a second, also has to be dispersed.

Completely new designs of bogies were also required for the higher speeds, and the bolsterless type was adopted. The traction and braking forces are transmitted between the bogie and the car body by special linkages, while the vehicle's weight is supported by air springs. These are, however, not mounted on the bolster as previously, but are attached directly to the bogie frame. This required the development of more flexible and durable air springs, the new bogies being tested extensively on some Series 100 cars as well as experimental vehicles. The air bags are equipped with valves to maintain the body at a constant height above the rails. If more passengers get on, the body sinks slightly and the valve opens to allow more air into the spring, which restores the body to its normal position. Air is similarly be let out if the weight is reduced as passengers get off. Such arrangements are fairly universal with modern suspensions, starting in the UK with the Mk IIIs.

To help reduce the new vehicles' weights, smaller wheels and hollow axles were fitted. Both of these also have a beneficial effect on the riding of the vehicles, as they cannot be cushioned from any rail irregularities by springing. The gear ratio between the traction motors and axles was increased from 1:2.41 to 1:2.96, which contributed to the reduction in motor size and weight by reducing the torque required for a given power output at the same track speed.

As with the earlier trains, the Series 300s can use their traction motors as brakes, but the a.c. design has an important advantage. Instead of having to dissipate the energy in a rheostat, and so wasting it by warming up the atmosphere, it can be returned to the overhead wire by the control circuits. These can be switched from one mode to the other almost instantaneously by the control computer, the process being known as regeneration. The equipment can maintain a power factor of unity at all times, thus utilising all the energy in the alternating current, which is important from the overall efficiency point of view.

The trailer cars on the Series 300s are equipped with eddy current disc brakes, but the retarding equipment on all the axles includes a feature which is not normally provided on express passenger trains. Load-response devices

Table 8.3
Comparisons between Shinkansen Traction Motors

			Series 0		Series 100		Series 300		Series 700	
Weight	kg	(lb)	876	(1930)	825	(1817)	450	(991)	391	(861)
Output	kW	(h.p.)	185	(248)	230	(308)	300	(402)	275	(369)
Specific weight	kg/kW	(lb/h.p.)	4.74	(7.72)	3.59	(5.89)	1.50	(2.46)	1.42	(2.34)
Outside diameter	mm	(ins)	580	(22.8)	580	(22.8)	484	(19.1)	484	(19.1)
Length	mm	(ins)	743	(29.3)	716	(28.2)	489	(19.3)	497	(19.6)
Volume	m³	(ft³)	0.196	(6.91)	0.189	(6.66)	0.090	(3.17)	0.090	(3.17)

Source: JR-C

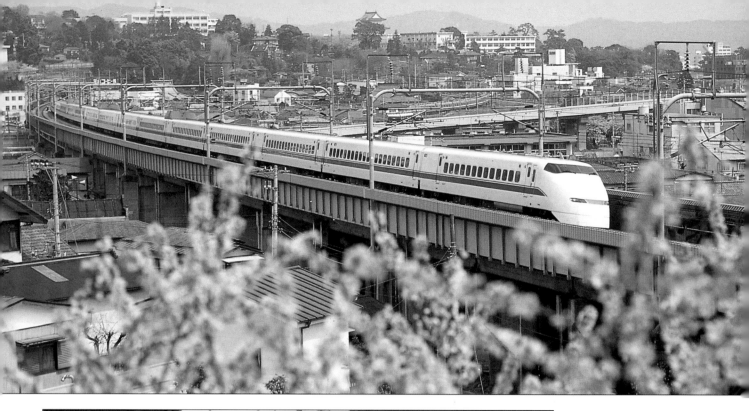

Above: Series 300 and peach blossom at Odawara. *Mikio Miura*

Right: Series 100 *Grand Hikari* passing Tokyo down-town with Japanese-gauge lines on the left. *Mikio Miura*

Left: A Series 100 Shinkansen enters Kyoto station with a down *Hikari* in October 1994.

Below: Sets of all three series of JR-Central's Shinkansen stabled at Oi Depot in Tokyo. *Mikio Miura*

Right: A Series 300 *Nozomi* passes the tea fields at Kakegawa. *Mikio Miura*

are fitted, which vary the braking on each bogie to match the load it is carrying. This is determined by the pressure in the air-bags, which is directly related to the weight on them by the action of the height-control valve described earlier. On freight vehicles the difference between the loaded and unloaded weights on an axle can be huge, and it is vital to control the retardation to prevent skidding the wheels if too great a braking force is applied. The same can apply to commuter trains with high crush-loadings, but the variation in axle loadings on express passenger trains is usually small enough not to justify the complications of varying the brake pressure in this way. A Series 300 car, however, with a maximum axle-load of only 10.1 tonnes, can seat as many as 100 passengers. At 15 to the tonne plus luggage, they could add more than seven extra tonnes to the overall weight of the 40-tonne vehicle – nearly a fifth. With the need to maximise braking efficiency to ensure that minimum time is lost slowing for stops, it was worth fitting the load-response equipment.

As a result of these changes in design, the Series 300s are far more energy efficient, in spite of having a higher installed traction power than either of the earlier designs. Table 8.4 shows how power consumptions vary with speed and train type for journeys over the Tokaido Shinkansen.

It will be seen how much more energy-efficient the Series 300 trains are, particularly when compared with the original ones, which used more energy for a journey at 220 km/h than one of the third-generation required when running 50 km/h faster. Faster trains are thus not necessarily profligate with energy. Table 8.5 shows further comparisons between the three different generations of train. By this time JR-C was confident of its new design, but before it could go into service various infrastructure changes would be necessary.

The first involved the overhead wiring, which had to withstand the passage of pantographs at speeds that were nearly 25% higher than previously. Traffic had grown and was likely to increase further, so the system was switched from the booster transformer (BT) system to the auto-transformer arrangement (AT), as used on the subsequent Shinkansen and for the French TGVs. This enables higher power inputs to be provided for extra trains, at the same time keeping trackside electrical interference to a minimum. There has to be a second, feeder cable for each track, but this can be kept clear of the actual catenary system. On the TGV lines these cables are slung from insulators hung from brackets on the outside of the masts. The Japanese have in places mounted theirs above the pipe beams, suspended from insulators hanging inside rectangular frames.

The actual overhead wiring also had to be upgraded again, with a composite contact wire being introduced where necessary. There are two versions of this, both containing a steel core, which enables the tension to be increased to benefit current-collection stability. The CSD170 mm design

has a circular core, and the shape of the outer copper sheath is similar to the higher-duty type installed for 220km/h running, making its weight virtually identical. The alternative TA200 design has a steel core which is rectangular in shape, with the long sides vertical, and the actual contact material around it is aluminium, giving a lighter wire, which is still capable of being highly tensioned.

Other things being equal, putting a train's speed up from 220 to 270 km/h increases the braking distance by 50%, so clearly there would have to be major changes to the ATC system before the Series 300s came into regular service. At the same time it was decided to use a dual-frequency arrangement for the modulated track-circuits. The following series of speed limits have now to be applied along the Tokaido line, for use when approaching an occupied section, or for permanent speed restrictions:

km/h	270	255	230	220	170	120	70	30
m.p.h.	168	158	143	137	106	75	43	19

New-style speedometers have been provided on all trains from Series 300 onwards, and the displays also include digital indications of the actual and 'target' speeds. There is still no cruise-control system.

After several years of development work and design, the decision to build a prototype Series 300 was taken early in 1988, and construction began the following year, with the unit being completed in March 1990. Within a few months trials began, and the first speed milestone was reached in July that year when the set attained its designed service speed, chalking up a maximum of 272 km/h (169 m.p.h.). In following December the train did even better and reached 303.1 km/h (188.3 m.p.h.), but this was eclipsed in February 1991 when it achieved 325.7 km/h (202.4 m.p.h.). It was not only the riding and performance of the vehicles that was being tested, as extensive measurements were made of the lineside noise and vibration. With orders placed for some production sets, long-term durability trials then began, and more than 270 000 km (168 000 miles) of test running between Tokyo and Shin-Osaka were carried out for this purpose alone.

By that time the new train had begun to be referred to as the *Super Hikari*, but before commercial services began, the trains were officially given the name *Nozomi* ('Hope'). Internally the layout was generally similar to the previous trains, but the weight-saving continued with the design of the seats. These came down to 12 kg each compared with the previous 28 (26 lb compared with 62), which, when multiplied by the 1323 provided, represented a total saving of over 20 tons or half a coach. It also proved possible to reduce the internal noise levels, both from the vehicles' underfloor equipment as well as the track, the former having been somewhat intrusive on the earliest designs. The proportion of Green Car accommodation increased, reflecting the train's intended clientele, and passengers in those vehicles could be served with meals at their seats by the hostesses. Elsewhere there are two snack counters, in addition to the usual vending trolleys passing up and down the train.

In March 1992 a pair of the new trains began operating two daily services in each direction between Tokyo and Shin-Osaka, out in the morning and back in the evening. The westbound working left the capital at 06.00 and the corresponding eastbound train departed from Osaka 12 minutes later. The evening workings both left at 21.18, although, to be strictly correct, the eastbound one was booked to start 30 seconds after this! Working times throughout were to quarter-minutes.

Table 8.4
Power Consumptions for Single Journey between Tokyo and Shin-Osaka

(*Hikari* services with intermediate stops at Nagoya and Kyoto)

Series	Maximum Speed (km/h)	(m.p.h.)	Power Consumption (kWh)
0	220	137	23 200
100	220	137	18 800
300	220	137	16 600
300	270	168	21 200

Source: JR-C

Table 8.5
Comparative statistics for Series 300, 100 and 0 Train-Sets

Model	Series 300	Series 100	Series 0
Electrical System	AC 25kV·60Hz	AC 25kV·60Hz	AC 25kV·60Hz
Configuration	10M6T	12M4T	16M
Nominal riding capacity	Ordinary: 1123 1st class: 200	Ordinary: 1153 1st class: 168	Ordinary: 1208* 1st class: 132
Weight (t/trainset loaded)	710	925	970
Maximum Speed (km/h, m.p.h.)	270/168	220/137	220/137
Balancing speed on level (km/h, m.p.h.)	296/184	276/172	235/146
Starting acceleration (km/h/s)	1.6	1.6	1.0
Power control system	VVVF+GTO.	Thyristor, continous. phase.	Low-voltage taps control.
Brake systems	AC regenerative + elec.actuated. air (T cars eddy current) Continuous control on adhesion pattern.	Rheostatic + elec.actuated. air (T cars eddy current) Continuous control on adhesion pattern.	Rheostatic + electro- magnetic straight air Control on ATC steps.
Body construction	Aluminum alloy Equipment underslung, interspersed with dummy plates.	Steel Equipment underslung, interspersed with dummy plates.	Steel Equipment underslung.
Body dimensions Length x Width x Height (m) End cars Intermediate car Bilevel car	 25.80 x 3.38 x 3.36 24.50 x 3.38 x 3.65 -	 25.80 x 3.38 x 4.00 24.50 x 3.38 x 4.00 24.50 x 3.38 x 4.49	 2.490 x 3.38 x 3.975 24.50 x 3.38 x 3.975 -
Body dimensions Length x Width x Height (ft) End cars Intermediate car Bilevel car	 84.6 x 11.1 x 12.0 80.4 x 11.1 x 13.1 -	 84.6 x 11.1 x 13.1 80.4 x 11.1 x 13.1 80.4 x 11.1 x 14.7	 81.7 x 11.1 x 13.0 80.4 x 11.1 x 13.0 -
Bogie	Wheel diam: 0.86m (33.9in.) Wheelbase: 2.50m (8.2ft) Bolsterless, no end beams.	Wheel diam: 0.86m (33.9in.) Wheelbase: 2.50m (8.2ft) Bolster with end beams.	Wheel diam: 0.86m(33.9in.) Wheelbase: 2.50m (8.2ft) Bolster with end beams.
Traction motors	AC 3-phase cage, asynchronous TMT3 (TMT4) 40 motors/train-set 300 kW/402 h.p./motor 12 000 kW/16 086h.p./train Force ventilated.	DC series-wound MT202 48 motors/train 230 kW/308 h.p./motor 11 040 kW/14 800 h.p./train Force ventilated.	DC series-wound MT200B 64 motors/train 185kW/248hp/motor 11 840kW/15,871hp/train Self-ventilated.
Gear ratio	1:2.96 (23:68)	1:2.41 (27:65)	1:2.17 (29:63)
Auxiliary power	Stationary-voltage stabilizer AC-DC100V Aux. transformer AC100V Tertiary winding AC 440V	Stationary-voltage stabilizer AC-DC100V Aux. transformer AC100V Tertiary winding AC 440V	Motor generator AC100V Auxiliary rectifier DC100V Auxiliary inverter AC100V Tertiary winding AC220V
Pantograph	TPS203 (Double-factor, suspended) 2 pantographs/train-set.	PS202 (Double-factor, suspended) 3 pantographs/train-set.	PS200 (Double-factor, suspended) 8 pantographs/train-set.

* In 1996, the Series 0 sets used for *Kodama* had a total of 1385 seats.

Source: JR-C, JR-W

The journey times dropped to 2½ hours, which corresponded to an overall average of 128.1 m.p.h. (206.2 km/h), although the eastbound morning train needed an extra 30 sec to slide itself into one of the platforms at Tokyo Central. Three of the trains made the traditional *Hikari* stops at Nagoya and Kyoto, but the morning departure from Tokyo called at Shin-Yohokama and then ran non-stop to Shin-Osaka. The fastest start-to-stop average was booked for the eastbound evening train, which achieved 225.4 km/h (140.1 m.p.h.) between Kyoto and Nagoya.

This service was clearly aimed at the 'out-and-back-in-a-day' business market, but the timetable was completely recast in March 1993, with hourly *Nozomi* services in each direction between Tokyo and Hakata, normally leaving Tokyo at 00.56, and the Kyushu terminus at 00.20. Trials of the trains west of Shin-Osaka had begun in the first half of 1992, and JR-West purchased nine Series 300 sets of their own in 1993 and 1994. End-to-end timings came down to as little as 5hrs 4min for the 1,069.1 km (664.3 miles), corresponding to an overall average of 211.0 km/h (131.1 m.p.h.). The trains proved very popular and extra

Stations and Track Layout on the Tokaido Shinkansen

Power supply	25 kV AC 60 Hz
Gauge	1,435 mm
Level crossings	0
Stations	16

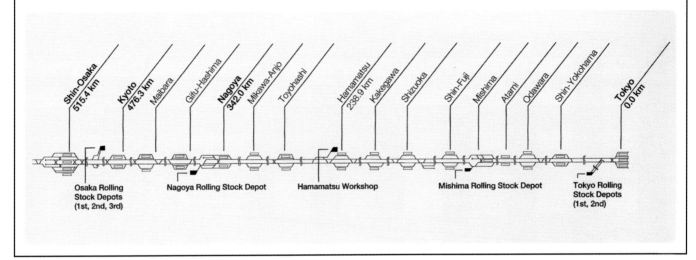

Osaka Rolling Stock Depots (1st, 2nd, 3rd) — Nagoya Rolling Stock Depot — Hamamatsu Workshop — Mishima Rolling Stock Depot — Tokyo Rolling Stock Depots (1st, 2nd)

surcharges were payable. All seats had to be reserved, and the Japan Rail Pass was not valid for travel on them, even if the appropriate supplement had been paid.

The changes in the two companies' Shinkansen car fleets to 1996 are summarised in Table 8.6. It will be seen that on the Tokaido Shinkansen the total number of cars has remained fairly constant since 1992, the increased numbers of Series 300 vehicles being matched by the decline of the oldest Series 0 ones. It should be noted that the totals for the two newer designs were both divisible by 16, showing they are kept as whole sets. The same did not apply with the remnant of the original design, of which a grand total of 3216 cars was built. There were various spare vehicles in the depots as individual cars reached the end of their economic life.

The percentage increase in the number of cars owned by JR-West was appreciably less than the corresponding figure for JR-Central, but the ratio of annual passenger-numbers to cars for the two companies are remarkably close. As with the JR-Central trains, the number of the JR-West cars of the newer series match the 16-car sets as used in service, but the average number of Series 0 cars per train on their system was only just over 10. Unlike their partners east of Osaka, they regularly scheduled the use of some shorter sets, such as the six-car *Family Hikari* trains operated during the summer.

With traffic booming, especially at the Tokyo end of the line, arrangements were made to increase the frequency of departures. With the start of the *Nozomi* services in March 1993, improvements made it possible to dispatch no less than 11 trains an hour from the three double-sided Tokaido Shinkansen platforms at Central Station. A *Nozomi* left at four minutes before the hour, and, in the hour until the next one departed, up to ten other trains could leave, so the service was referred to as '1N-7H-3K'. This was a remarkable achievement, as within little more than a train's

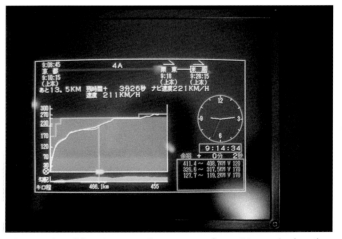

Above: Driver's speedometer of *Nozomi* on the occasion of the author's cab journey described in this chapter. The ATC is permitting a maximum of 255 km/h, as shown by the illuminated disc and the smaller figure on the bottom of the screen. By that time the train had accelerated to 232 km/h, as marked by the end of the red line and the larger digital display at the bottom. *JR-Central*

Above: The driver's secondary screen for a *Nozomi*, showing the comprehensive display of information. The blue area indicates the permitted speed, and it will be seen that an increase to 270 km/h will be allowed shortly. The vertical white line indicates where the train is at the present time, and the two white traces slanting upwards show the required and achieved acceleration curves. *JR-Central*

length from the 'country ends' of the platforms, the six tracks have converged to a simple pair, with a scissors-crossover providing the ability for arriving and departing trains to use any of the platforms. In normal conditions the services are so well regulated that the track (platform) used by each particular train at the major stations can be indicated in the timetable.

During the late 1990s work was put in hand to increase the number of trains that can be operated in and out of Tokyo at peak periods. Four of the hourly arrivals of Shinkansen sets at Tokyo have to visit Oi depot for servicing, and these empty workings currently occupy some of the slots on the main line. To avoid this loss of capacity, a new *through* station is being built at Shinagawa, approx 7 km towards Yokohama, a short distance beyond the spur to the Ooi rolling-stock depot, as shown in the illustration. With some turn-back sidings at the Tokyo end, a pair of new island platforms will provide four more tracks where trains can terminate and start their return journeys. These are situated alongside the existing station on the 'Japanese-gauge' lines which will provide connections to and from various parts of Tokyo. When the new station is completed, provisionally in the financial year 2003/04, it will be possible to despatch a combined total of no less than 15 Shinkansen services an hour from it and Tokyo Central station, as well as handling a similar number of arrivals.

Table 8.7 gives a breakdown of the regular service trains in 1996 on the Tokaido and Sanyo Lines, showing the numbers of the different types run and the sections of the combined route they served. These have been taken from the 1996 pocket timetable, and only include those trains which ran every day Mondays to Fridays, holidays excepted. There were many more seasonal trains, but the frequency with which they operated is not indicated in the timetable. The Shinkansen Control Rooms collect the information on how many trains operate each day, from which can be worked out the average daily totals. Mention is made later of these latter figures.

In the regular timetable, there were 38 *Nozomi*, 177 *Hikari* and 169 *Kodama* workings every day, giving a grand total of 384. The majority of the *Nozomi* worked through between the two companies' metals, but only 40% of the *Hikari* did so, nearly half the total remaining on the Tokaido section. As one would expect, through-running *Kodama* are

Diagram showing location and layout of new Tokaido Shinkansen station at Shinagawa in Tokyo, with details of maximum hourly train movements.

Right: On a snowy day in January 1988, a JR-West Series 500 passes the site of the new Shingawa station in Tokyo, showing how close it will be to the 'Japanese-gauge' suburban station in the background.
Mikio Miura

Table 8.6
Tokaido & Sanyo Shinkansen Numbers of Coaches 1987–1996

Tokaido Shinkansen
Series

Year	0	100	300	TOTAL
1987	1343	112	-	1454
1988	1307	160	-	1467
1989	1281	352	-	1633
1990	1190	608	16	1814
1991	1064	832	16	1912
1992	1005	912	80	1997
1993	898	912	240	2050
1994	775	912	336	2023
1995	667	912	432	2011
1996	542	912	576	2021

Source: JR-C

Sanyo Shinkansen
Series

Year	0	100N	300	500	TOTAL
1987	715	-	-	-	715
1988	715	-	-	-	715
1989	693	32	-	-	725
1990	667	64	-	-	731
1991	656	112	-	-	768
1992	623	144	-	-	767
1993	574	144	80	-	798
1994	546	144	144	-	834
1995	536	144	144	-	824
1996	522	144	144	16	826

Source: JR-W

Table 8.7
Daily Numbers of Trains on Tokaido and Sanyo Shinkansen, 1996
(Regular service trains, Mondays to Fridays)

	Nozomi	*Hikari*	*Kodama*	TOTAL
WESTBOUND				
Tokaido Line only	3	41	36	80
Through services	15	33	1	49
Sanyo Line only	1	14	48	63
TOTALS	19	88	85	192
EASTBOUND				
Tokaido Line only	3	40	41	84
Through services	14	38	1	53
Sanyo Line only	2	11	42	55
TOTALS	19	89	84	192
GRAND TOTALS	38	177	169	384

Source: JR-Group Timetable 2000

very much the exception, with only one such working a day in each direction out of the 169. The total number of Shinkansen regular trains operating on the Tokaido line came to 266 daily, compared with 220 on the Sanyo route. The railways' ticket analyses showed the proportion of through passengers between the two high-speed lines, but this suddenly became very obvious to the travelling public in early 1995, when the Great Hanshin Earthquake severed the east end of the Sanyo Shinkansen for several weeks.

If the seasonal trains are added, the average daily totals for 1996 were as follows:

Tokaido Shinkansen	283	*Nozomi*	37
Sanyo Shinkansen	228	*Hikari*	187
TOTAL	401	*Kodama*	177
		TOTAL	401

In the course of time the calling patterns for the different services had changed somewhat from the original simple one involving hourly *Hikari* and *Kodama* workings. In addition to stopping at Nagoya and Kyoto, many of the *Hikari* were calling at other intermediate stations, Shin-Yokohama being the most common one on the Tokaido Shinkansen. Several, however, also stopped at both intermediate stations between Nagoya and Kyoto and Gifu-Hashima and Maibara – and many then also called at all stations on to Okayama after the crew change. There were also a number of daily stops at Shizuoka and Hamamatsu. Quite a lot of the 'through trains' from Tokyo listed in Table 8.7 only ran as far as Okayama, rather than all the way to Hakata.

The *Kodama* services in and out of Tokyo were serving the three new stations east of Nagoya which were opened in 1988. As the number of *Hikari* and *Nozomi* expresses increased, the loops at these stations provided additional opportunities for the stopping trains to be overtaken, but some

of the *Kodama* now had to stand for longer than they used to do at intermediate stations waiting for paths forward.

The successful and safe operation of any railway requires an organisation to carry out the necessary servicing and maintenance on the rolling stock. Although the Japanese railways are developing suburban trains which require very little such attention, this cannot yet be contemplated for the high-speed Shinkansen units. Table 8.8 shows the cycle of inspections and overhauls for the Series 300 sets.

The Tokaido Shinkansen workshop is located at Hamamatsu, some 257 km (160 miles) from Tokyo, but there are no less than seven rolling-stock depots. They are situated as follows, listed from east to west:

Tokyo (Oi)
First
Second
Nagoya
Osaka (Torigai)
First
Second
Third

It may seem surprising that there are as many as three in one city, but with the 1996 totals of 57 Series 100 sets, 36 Series 300s, and more than 30 of the original Series 0s, each of them a quarter of a mile long, to stable and inspect overnight, a lot of space was needed, and some spent the night in the platforms at Tokyo Central. Marshalled end-to-end, JR-Central's Shinkansen fleet would at that time have stretched for some 30 miles or nearly 50 km! A total of 2300 staff is employed at the depots and workshop. On the Sanyo Shinkansen, JR-West's Shinkansen workshop and depot is located south of Hakata, and they also have depots at Okayama and Hiroshima.

Table 8.8
Servicing and Overhaul Schedules for Series 300 Shinkansen in 1997

Frequency	Type of Inspection	Where Done
Daily	Pre-service	Rolling-stock depot
30 000 km or 30 days*	Regular	Rolling-stock depot
450 000 km or 12 months*	Bogies	Rolling-stock depot
900 000 km or 36 months*	Overhaul	Workshop

* whichever comes first.

Source: JR-C

Table 8.9
Fastest Shinkansen Start-to-Stop Speeds: 1993–1999

Year	Train	From[1]	To[1]	Distance km	miles	Time min	Speed km/h	mph
1993	27 *Nozomi*	Hiroshima	Kokura	192.0	119.3	50	230.4	143.2
1995	31 *Nozomi*	Hiroshima	Kokura	192.0	119.3	50	230.4	143.2

[1] Some of the journeys were in the opposite direction.

Source: *Railway Gazette International.*

Table 8.10
Fastest Shinkansen Journeys, 1987–1999

Year	Train	From	To	Distance km	miles	Time hr	min	No. of Stops	Speed km/h	mph
1987	1 *Hikari*	Hakata	Shin-Osaka	553.7	306.3	3	02	3	182.5	113.4
1993	1 *Nozomi*	Hakata	Shin-Osaka	553.7	306.3	2	32	3	218.6	135.8

Source: *Railway Gazette International.*

The view through the sloping windscreen was much better than expected from the external appearance, but the blue-tinted area at the top and the unit's number in the bottom right-hand corner made it difficult to photograph the procession of trains in the opposite direction. The 83.4 miles from Kyoto to Nagoya were covered in 36min 49sec, at an average start-to-stop speed of 136.0 m.p.h. (218.9 km/h), inclusive of the permanent-way slowing.

The introduction of the faster *Nozomi* brought the Tokaido and Sanyo Shinkansen back into the *Railway Gazette International's* two-yearly world speed reviews, after being ousted by the faster services on the Tokohu and Joetsu Shinkansen from 1985 onwards. Tables 8.9 and 8.10 list the fastest station-to-station runs and the fastest overall journeys. The higher design speed of the Sanyo Shinkansen has resulted in all these entries being for trains which run at least in part over JR-West's tracks.

One of the outstanding aspects of performance on the Tokaido and Sanyo Shinkansen has been punctuality. Long before BR organised its TRUST system for automatically reporting train times, the Shinkansen Control Centres were regularly recording the detailed running of every train. The Japanese target is to be on time, and there is no 'within 10 minutes of booked time' standard as there is with Intercity trains in the UK. They accordingly report the overall average lateness, which is the lost time divided by the number of trains, and the answer is quoted in *seconds*. The figures in Table 8.11 are for the Tokaido Shinkansen up to 1996. It will be seen that there was a bad spell in the late 1970s/early 1980s, but since then some remarkable figures were achieved.

The benefits resulting from the development of the Series 300 Shinkansen were summed up at the 'S-tech '96' International Conference at Birmingham in September 1996, its theme being 'Better Journey Time – Better Business'. In his address, Mr H Soejima, then Vice-President of JR-Central, said that introducing the *Nozomi* involved an investment of ¥ 120 billion, but the faster and more frequent services had increased the railway's revenue by approximately ¥ 15 billion a year, giving an annual return of about 12½%. Such a rate would be very welcome with a savings account, let alone a transport investment.

In 1994 the writer travelled in the cab of an eastbound *Nozomi* from Kyoto one Sunday morning, joining the driver during the stop there. The Series 300s have a video screen alongside the speedometer, which provides the driver with additional information to enable him to optimise the train's operation. While we were standing in the station, the screen was showing a count-down of the seconds before we were due to depart, but the actual signal to start is still given by the senior conductor. When the power controller has been moved, the video screen changes, to show the speed profile of the line ahead. The permitted maximum is shown by a blue block up from the bottom of the 'graph', and a slanting white line across it indicates the acceleration required to maintain the schedule. As we accelerated, a second such line was plotted progressively, showing the driver how closely he matched the target, and the whole display scrolls along as the train progresses.

There is another video screen on the right of the driver, which provides diagnostic displays, in similar fashion to the those on the German ICEs and many other modern trains. Leaving Kyoto there was a change-over section in the overhead wiring, and a display was selected to show the action of the circuit-breakers along the quarter-mile length of our train. There is no actual neutral section, as in the UK, and the intermediate stretch of the catenary is connected to one or other of the circuits on either side, the change-over taking place within about 0.3 seconds, without disturbing the electrical supply system on the train.

This run took place over the stretch where JR-Central carry out their high-speed trials, which we will be discussing in Chapter 10, but as early as 28 February 1991 the prototype Series 300 reached 325.7 km/h (202.4 m.p.h.) along here. On the writer's run the train passed Maibara in 18½min from Kyoto, having averaged 137m.p.h. from the start. The previous *Kodama* departure, which had left Kyoto 14min ahead of us, was tucked into the Tokyo-bound platform loop, waiting for us to pass. It was hereabouts that a lower permitted speed suddenly appeared on the right-hand side of the video screen, and the whole of the area below it accordingly turned red. This indicated there was a temporary permanent-way slowing ahead, and gave the driver advance warning before the ATC called for the usual braking procedure.

Table 8.11
Tokaido Shinkansen Train Punctuality

Year (ending 31 March)	Average Lateness (seconds)
1965	71
1970	87
1975	387
1980	159
1985	52
1990	39
1996	53

Staff

Top left: A Series 300 is waved off by the station supervisor. *Mikio Miura*

Above: The conductor keeps an eye on passengers leaving and boarding the train. *Mikio Miura*

Left: The driver of a *Hikari* brakes the train for a station stop. *Mikio Miura*

Bottom left: The Purser in an ordinary car of Series 300. *Mikio Miura*

Below: The conductor, in his summer uniform, uses the internal telephone to speak to the driver. *JR-Central*

CHAPTER 9
JR-East Shinkansen Developments

The Privatisation of JNR in 1987 resulted in the East Japan Railway becoming, not only the largest of the new Japanese companies, but the biggest passenger railway in the world. To get some idea of the size of its business, it handles approximately *twice* the number of passengers that travel on the German, French, Swiss and British railways *combined*. They achieved a total of 6.0 billion passengers for the year 1992/93, when their staff numbered just under 80 000. In the UK our nationalised railways moved 745 million passengers that year, but had a total of 138 000 staff.

The main reason behind these vastly different figures is the Tokyo commuter, as JR-East has an enormous share of the daily traffic in and out of the capital, and has built special double-deck Shinkansen stock for this purpose. Although in competition with ten private railways, including the Metro, JR-East earns almost half of the total commuter revenue because its routes stretch out further than those of the other lines. They also have the very important Japanese-gauge Yamanote Line loop, 34.5 km (21.4 miles) long, which encircles the central area, and provides an important distribution system. Figure 9.1 gives an idea of incoming passenger flows each weekday morning. Not only is Tokyo Central on the loop, but seven of the company's ten busiest stations are served by it. Shinjuku tops the list and handles a daily total of over three-quarters of a million passengers. (In 1989 the whole of BR's Network SouthEast carried only 2 million passengers a day).

From April 1987 JR-East leased the Tohoku and Joetsu Shinkansen from the Shinkansen Holding Corporation, but, as described in Chapter 7, in October 1991 the infrastructure of these was purchased for just over ¥3000 billion. Such a sum may seem astronomic, but it was only approximately three-quarters of their original construction cost. This increased the railway's long-term debt by just over 100%, with the majority of the payments being spread out until 2017, although it will be 2053 before the final instalment is paid off. (This is standard Japanese procedure with such loans, and interest is charged on the outstanding amounts).

The passenger numbers using the Shinkansen services only form 1% of JR-East's total, but they currently contribute an eighth of the total passenger-kilometres, and roughly the same proportion of the company's total railway receipts. This represented a considerable improvement on the figure immediately prior to Privatisation, the income having risen by a third in the four years from 1987. The two high-speed lines had a combined length of 838.9 km (521.3 miles) out of the railway's total 7567 route-kilometres (4702 miles).

From the point of view of JR-East's Shinkansen, at the time of Privatisation there was still an important item of unfinished business – the completion of the link from Ueno into Tokyo Central station. It was only in August 1986 that the government had given permission for the work to be restarted the following year. Although no more than 3.6 km (2.2 miles) long, it was a major civil engineering task, with a unit-cost roughly ten times that for a contemporary high-speed line through the open countryside. There is a steep climb from the depths of Ueno station on to a viaduct parallel to the '1067mm-gauge' tracks of the Yamanote Loop.

The job was expected to be completed in 1989 but it was not until June 1991 that JR-East's Shinkansen were able to start using the capital's main station. Initially their trains only had access to a single island platform, with track numbers 12 and 13 either side of it, so some smart operating was needed at peak periods. In the mid-1990s work began to build an additional, elevated, two-sided platform, which was constructed behind the brick-red facade of the station building. This did not actually handle the steadily-increasing numbers of Shinkansen trains, but was used for the ordinary trains on the Ou line. The track in the latter's existing twin platforms were relaid to standard-gauge, which doubled the space available for the Shinkansen services.

During the latter half of the 1980s a lot of thought nationally had been given to how it would be possible to extend the Shinkansen network at a cost the country could afford, and two alternatives were developed to do this incrementally. The existence of the two different gauges was the fundamental problem. As had been realised when the original Tokaido Shinkansen was being planned, a new facility could not be brought into use progressively by widening an existing '1067 mm-gauge' line, because no through running would be possible until it had been converted in its entirety.

It was the pending completion of the extremely-costly Seikan Tunnel connecting Honshu and Hokkaido that brought the matter to a head, details of which are given elsewhere. The 53.85-km (33.5-mile) tunnel had originally been planned as part of the 1970s' Shinkansen route from Tokyo to Sapporo, which had subsequently been cut back to Morioka on cost grounds. When the tunnel was finished in 1988 there was going to be a gap of some 150 miles (240 km) between its southern portal and the nearest Shinkansen railhead. It was therefore decided to provide facilities for mixed-gauge track through the bore, which raised some interesting problems with track-circuits. The solutions adopted were described in one of the papers delivered at the first overseas conference held by the Railway Division of the UK 'Mechanicals' at Le Touquet in 1992. Even when standard-gauge trains begin running through it, there will still be a need for '1067mm-gauge' tracks for freight trains, and the latter rails were laid first. The loading-gauge is quite large enough to permit the passage of Shinkansen stock in due course, and the alignment enables faster speeds than usual to be reached by the '1067mm-gauge' trains. Thus was born the 'Super-Express' idea for piecemeal extension of the Shinkansen system.

The 'Super-Express' concept involves the building of new lines along the route of future Shinkansen. They would be laid out to the full high-speed standards of loading-gauge, curvature, etc, with provision for the track gauge to be widened at some future time and the overhead wiring altered. The classic trains using them in the meanwhile were less noisy and produced less vibration, so it would not be necessary to provide the costly full environmental protection until the section was upgraded. Although the *full* potential of the new facilities would not immediately be utilised, this type of line, with a maximum speed of 200km/h (125 m.p.h.), would provide significant reductions in journey times. In this way the initial capital cost would be reduced and the total expenditure spread over a longer period.

Top Left: The view from a Series 400 Shinkansen travelling north on the elevated tracks of the Tohoku Shinkansen between Ueno and Omiya. On the other track a Series 200 train heads for Tokyo.

Above: Mixed gauge track between Yamagata and Zao.

Left: JR-East F-fleet set No. 19 in Platform 22 at Tokyo Central station in October 1994, with the Japanese-gauge suburban tracks on the right. Note the door-position markers on the surface of the platform and the row of warning lights nearer the edge which flash when a train is due to arrive. The cranes in the background were working on the construction of the new platforms for the Hokuriku Shinkansen.

Left: A Standard-Gauge local EMU at Kaminoyama on the Yamagata Line. The reconstructed station building includes a Community Plaza.

Below: Tendo station north of Yamagata on the Ou Line. The building houses the Japanese Chess Museum and the paving makes the square look like a large chessboard.

Right: The driver's controls on a production Series E3 'Mini-Shinkansen'. The power controller is the black, cross-headed, handle which moves fore-and-aft in the control panel. The round-headed knob on the right controls the direction of travel. The brake lever is on the left of the panel, hidden by the driver. *Mikio Miura*

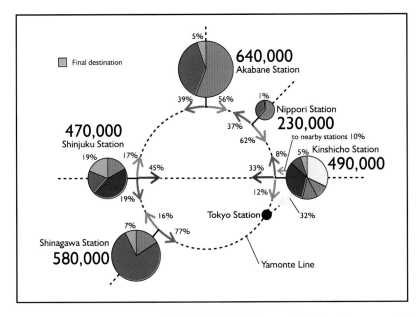

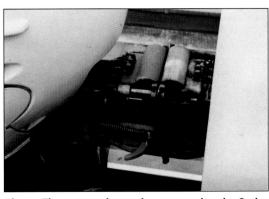

Above: The automatic couplers connecting the Series 200 (left) with the Series 400 'Mini-Shinkansen' (right).

Figure 9.1 (left): The daily incoming commuter flow into Tokyo on JR-East's lines in 1991. The colours in the pie-charts show the proportions of onward passengers travelling in the direction of the same-coloured arrows.

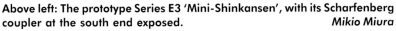

Above left: The prototype Series E3 'Mini-Shinkansen', with its Scharfenberg coupler at the south end exposed. *Mikio Miura*

Above right: The front end of a production 'Mini-Shinkansen' Series E3 *Komachi* at its press launch in December 1996. The shape and the position of the headlights differ slightly from the prototype. These units are due to enter service between Tokyo and Akita via Morioka on 22 March 1997. The fastest services will take 3 hours 49 minutes, with the trains being combined with a Series 200 or E2' *Yamabiko* set on the main line. *Mikio Miura*

Right: The eye-catching clock-tower in the square outside the reconstructed station at Yamagata.

In 1991 the 'Super-Express' idea was planned to be used as part of three separate extensions, and formal 'start-of-work' ceremonies were held at each. One was in Kyushu, between Yatsushiro and Nishi Kagoshima, where the existing '1067mm-gauge' line will provide the link northwards to the western end of the Sanyo Shinkansen at Hakata. This route traverses an area of extremely complex geology, and the work on the 125.2 km (77.8 mile) line was expected to take some 10 years, and cost ¥457 billion at 1989 prices. At that time there were also proposals for some 'Super-Express' extensions to the proposed new Hokuriku Shinkansen along the coast of the Sea of Japan, linking Nagano with the Joetsu route, needed for the 1998 Winter Olympics being held near that city.

An alternative to the 'Super-Express' system is the 'Mini-Shinkansen', and work on the first of these was put in hand as early as November 1987. The concept had been planned in late JNR days, but the go-ahead had to await the formation of the East Japan Railway. The project involved converting and widening the track on an existing '1067mm.-gauge' line and linking it to the main Shinkansen network by a suitable junction. Special high-speed trains, with bodies built to Japanese '1067mm-gauge' dimensions, would be needed, capable of running at full speed on the Shinkansen line, either by themselves or coupled to a full-sized set. In appropriate places it would also be possible for the new stock to run at higher speeds on the converted line than had previously been possible.

The first of these 'Mini-Shinkansen' routes involved 90 km (56 miles) of the Ou Main line from Yamagata to Fukushima, which is situated on the Tohoku Shinkansen 255 km (158½ miles) from Tokyo Central. Two possibilities were considered, the first being to convert only one set of rails to standard gauge, so effectively having two separate parallel railways. There were, however, complications, as a third of the route was single track. Investigations showed it would be cheaper and more flexible to provide twin standard-gauge tracks for most, but not quite all, of the way. Even this caused a lot of work to avoid too much disruption, and the change-over took no less than four years to complete.

Work started in 1988, with one of the '1067mm-gauge' tracks being widened, while the existing trains continued to run on the other. When this was complete, the single-track stretch between Sekine and Nakagawa was closed completely for three months, and the link maintained by buses. A standard-gauge track was added alongside most of the single-track stretch, and the remainder widened. This was completed in 1991 and the services began throughout on the single standard-gauge track on 5 November that year, a few EMUs being fitted with new bogies and pantographs. Work then concentrated on regauging the second track. For most of the route it was only necessary to lay new sleepers, the existing rails being reused. It was also necessary to build a connecting viaduct with the Shinkansen line just north of Fukushima station, and modify the platform layout to permit sets to join or divide.

The route is an extremely exacting one, as it has to cross the Asahi mountains by the Itaya Pass, which involves a climb of some 600 metres (almost 2000 feet), the summit being reached less than 25 km (15 miles) from the junction. As a result the *ruling* gradients are as steep as 3.33% for considerable stretches – a formidable 1 in 30 – with some even steeper pitches. The original platforms at certain of the stations on the incline had even been built on level spurs off the main tracks, to ease the gradients in the

platforms and facilitate the starting of heavy trains. Some of them had also been provided with snow-sheds for protection in the winter.

At the Yamagata end of the converted line there was another complication which had to be dealt with. There are industrial facilities which rely on the railway to handle their freight traffic at Zao, 5.3 km (3¼ miles) along the line, so some mixed-gauge track is provided, complete with Brunel-inspired staggered cross-overs and turnouts.

To operate the new service, the Series 400 Shinkansen trains were designed. Their dimensions are smaller all round than those of the Series 200s used on the Tohoku Shinkansen. The overall width was reduced from 3380 to 2950 mm (11ft 1in to 9ft 8in), and the roof height was cut by 2¾in. The overall length of the intermediate cars is 20 m (65ft 7in). They had a much more streamlined appearance, the effect being enhanced by a twin-tone livery in metallic silver-grey, and they were initially referred to as 'Silver Stream 21'. Their official name later became *Tsubasa*, which is translated as 'Wings'. To avoid dangerous gaps between the coaches and the Shinkansen platforms, retractable bridging-plates automatically extend to cover them during station stops.

On the main Shinkansen tracks these units run at the usual speeds of up to 240 km/h (149 m.p.h.), taking 25 kV 50 Hz power from the overhead wires, but the equipment is switched to cope with the 20 kV available on the branch, where their maximum speed is 130 km/h (81 m.p.h.). This was a considerable lift from the previous 95 km/h (59 m.p.h.) maximum, although there are some stretches through the mountains where speed is still restrained by curves with radii as tight as 300 m (330 yards). Another constraint is caused by the existence of level crossings on the converted stretches, a feature which is totally absent from a normal Shinkansen route. The Series 400s thus have a row of four high-intensity headlights across the top of the windscreen to warn anyone foolish enough to stray on to the tracks at these points, a significant problem on the country's normal lines.

The sets originally consisted of six cars, all motored, but in 1995 a trailer was added to provide extra capacity. The power bogies are fitted with a 210 kW (280 h.p.) d.c. motor on each axle, driven by thyristor bridges, giving a total of 6730 h.p. The weight of the six-car trains was 278 tonnes, which rose to 318 when the additional trailer was added. So, with slightly more installed power available than a UK Class 91, the sets clearly have no difficulty in coping with the gradients as well as running at high speed. The prototype was completed as early as October 1990, and underwent nearly two years' intensive testing. In the course of this it set two new Japanese speed records, reaching 336 km/h (208.8 m.p.h.) in March 1991, followed by 345 km/h (214.4 m.p.h.) six months later. Both were achieved on the Joetsu Shinkansen. (See Table 10.2).

At Fukushima the branch-line trains only have access to the outside track of the northbound platform, which is reversibly signalled. From Tokyo, the 'Mini-Shinkansen' set is marshalled at the north end of a *Yamabiko* service to the north. When the train arrives at Fukushima the *Tsubasa* is uncoupled from the cab, without anyone having to get on to the track, and continues by itself to Yamagata. The reverse arrangement applies in the Tokyo-bound direction. The *Yamabiko* set arrives first and crosses all the tracks into Platform 14. After it has stopped at the usual marker, a supersonic signal is sent from the lineside to the rear car, which opens the cover hiding the Scharfenberg automatic coupler. The Series 400 arrives a few minutes later and halts at its marker, well clear of the other set, where another of the lineside devices opens the coupling cover on its leading coach. The driver then runs forward slowly to couple-up, the speed being monitored continuously and the brakes automatically applied if it gets too high. Once the electrical and pneumatic connections have been made and checked, the driver of the *Tsubasa* gets a signal to shut down his cab systems, and control is taken over by his colleague at the front of the full-size unit for the run to Tokyo.

The normal time from Tokyo to Yamagata prior to the start of the through services was 3hr 11min, of which 97min were spent on the Shinkansen route. Eleven minutes were required at Fukushima to change trains, and the '1067mm-gauge' journey took another 83 min. The fastest of the 15 daily journeys in each direction in the improved 1996 timetable was completed in 2hr 27min. Business has boomed as a result. In 1985 some 2600 daily passengers to and from the branch used the main-line Shinkansen trains, and it was estimated that, without the alterations, the total would only have increased to 3280 by 1993. A year after the new services began, the daily ridership was already 4420, and the air service from Yamagata to Tokyo had cut out one of its daily round trips. Most trains call at the four intermediate stations on the Ou Line, although there are peak-hour services which run non-stop. There is also one northbound morning train which does not include a Series 200 set, as well as a corresponding arrangement for the last southbound train of the day.

The writer had followed the 'Mini-Shinkansen' concept from a distance with great interest, and in October 1994 was able to make a round-trip from Tokyo to Yamagata as a guest of East Japan Railway, together with his wife. Miss Emiko Ito of their International Department acted as guide during the day, and we gathered at the north end of Platform 12 at Tokyo Central some time before the 08.36 combined departure of *Yamabiko 113/Tsubasa 113*. In the meanwhile it was extremely interesting to watch the frequent departures and arrivals taking place on the nearby platforms. Shortly before our train was due, one of the then-new MAX double-deck sets arrived in Platform 13, and disgorged its load of city-bound passengers. (These extremely-impressive trains will be described later in this chapter).

After our set had arrived and its passengers had alighted, the cleaners descended on it, but we did not have to wait before boarding, as we were to travel in the cab for the 109 km (68 miles) as far as Utsunomiya. We therefore joined Driver Oba, whom we discovered was due to retire within 12 months after 25 years at the front end. To conform to the rules, the three passengers put on green 'Velcro' armbands with the JR-E initials, which were our authority to travel in the cab. Just before the departure time there was the usual platform announcement about our train, preceded by a short piece of music. Each station on the Tohoku and Joetsu Shinkansen has its own tune, used to preface the on-train announcements as well, so regular travellers can identify where they are from what is being played, without waiting for the spoken word. As we found out later, inside the *Tsubasa* coaches there are dot-matrix displays on the end walls, which even convey news messages, as well as the movements of the Nikkei Index in the Tokyo stock exchange.

Back in 1982, when we had travelled on the Tohoku Shinkansen, we had to take a local train as far as Ueno, before picking up the Shinkansen Relay which conveyed us to Omiya to join the newly-opened high-speed line. Twelve years later we could make the through journey from Tokyo Central station, and from the cab were able to note the extremely difficult engineering that had made this possible. Not far from the platform-end we dived underground, and reached a maximum of 42 m.p.h. on the stretch to Ueno. After restarting we re-emerged into the open, before climbing on to the long viaduct to Omiya, with speed limited to 68 m.p.h. Although it took us nearly 25 minutes to cover this stretch, that was a lot quicker than it had been 12 years earlier, and saved two changes. Although our speed was restricted, we were nevertheless overtaking a succession of trains on the elevated Saikyo Line on our right. Finally we descended at 1 in 40 into Omiya station, where, after the stop, the fast running was to begin.

From the restart it only took 4½ minutes to reach 240 km/h (149 m.p.h.), less time than an InterCity 225 requires to attain 125mph southwards from York. Even so, our *Tsubasa*, and the *Yamabiko* behind us, had twice been eased because the next higher-speed indication had not yet appeared on the driver's ATC indicator. Apart from a short temporary speed restriction to 100 m.p.h. before Oyama, we then ran at a steady 240 km/h (149 m.p.h.) all the way until power was cut off for the Utsunomiya stop. Our average speed worked out at 117.7 m.p.h. (189.4 km/h), but this improved to 127.3 m.p.h. (204.9 km/h), start-to-stop, on the next stretch of 104.9 km (65.2 miles) to Koriyama.

All Japanese drivers are extremely good at stopping their trains very accurately in stations, so the queues of waiting passengers are in line with the doors. With the *Tsubasa* this is carried even further, as, not only is there a marker hung from the platform roof, but a pointer has been provided on the bottom edge of the cab window which has to be aligned with it. The reason for this is the gap between these narrower trains and the platforms, along which stainless-steel safety railings are provided as protection. There are openings in them opposite where the train doors will be, to enable the footsteps to bridge the gap after they have been extended from the train. Stops thus have to be made very accurately to achieve the correct alignment.

Our party had returned to the train by this time, and we found the Green Cars very comfortable, with reversible 2+1 seating, whereas the arrangement in the ordinary cars is 2+2. There is a trolley service, and we were offered a choice of free drinks, which included Japanese green tea as well as coffee. Cans of various sorts, including beer, were also available for purchase. The journey through the mountains was extremely interesting, with the steep gradients both sides of the Itaya Pass. We then reached the rich agricultural area of the Yamagata Prefecture, noted for its pears, grapes, cherries and rice, as well as the *sake* (rice wine) brewed from the grain.

Interesting though the provision of the through Shinkansen services was, the writer then discovered another aspect of JR-East's cooperative efforts. In collaboration with the prefecture and the communities along the line, most of the stations have been rebuilt, to provide additional facilities for those living nearby, as well as to attract tourists to the area. They include trade centres, community facilities, museums, a library, galleries and a theatre, information centres and a hot-spring resort. While some urban landscapes in Japan are not outstanding, architects of high repute were brought in to design the striking new buildings. To complement the Japanese Chess Museum at Tendo, for example, the open space outside station has appropriately been paved in large black and white squares, the open space being broken up with trees and architectural features.

Top: The first special train, with commemorative headboard, marking the final extension of the Tohoku and Joetsu Shinkansen from Ueno, climbs out of the tunnel on its way into Tokyo Central Station on 20 June 1991. *Mikio Miura*

Left: A Series 400 Shinkansen forges its way up a 1 in 62 incline on the Ou Line near Niwasaka. *Mikio Miura*

Below: The special bridging-plates of a Series 400 'Mini-Shinkansen' seen extended to cover the gap between the doorway and the edge of the ordinary Shinkansen platform. *Mikio Miura*

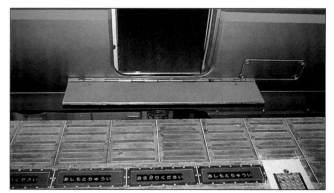

The instrument panel of *Tsubasa 113* travelling at 236km/h (147mph) on the occasion of the author's journey described in this chapter. The maximum speed of 240km/h permitted at that point by the ATC is also indicated.

Driver Oba at the controls of *Tsubasa 113* on the occasion of the author's cab journey.

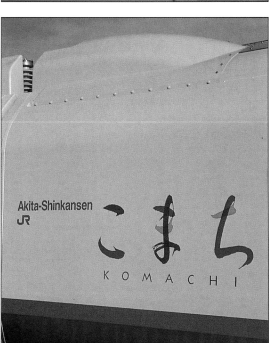

Above: A Series E3 *Komachi* set approaches Fukushima on a test run in December 1996.

Left: The production Series E3 'Mini-Shinkansen' are fitted with a new design of single-arm pantograph.

Above: Front view of one of the prototype JR-East Series E2' Shinkansen. This end of the set is not equipped with the Scharfenberg coupling.

Below: Interior of Green Car of prototype JR-East Series E2' set. *Mikio Miura* (5)

Above: The 'Mini-Shinkansen' Series E3 sets for the Tokyo–Akita services have been given the name *Komachi*, which is displayed on their bodywork in European as well as Japanese Hiragana lettering. Komachi Ono was a famous ninth-century poetess, also noted for her beauty. The Akita Prefecture is today well known for its many beautiful young girls, who are referred to as 'Akita Komachi.'

Investments such as those just described were paid for under the then-current financing arrangements for new Shinkansen lines, the cost of which was shared equally between public funds and the JR-Group. The former came from regional and government sources, and the split between them depended on the relative benefits for local and national interests. Station improvements came under the former heading, and were funded 25% from local sources, but in other places the local contribution could be as low as 10%. The JR-Group contributed in two different ways. The first was a somewhat roundabout one, as some 30% of the total cost came from the Railway Development Fund, referred to in Chapter 7, which received a further grant of ¥1000 billion from the government. This was topped up annually by depreciation charges on the original Shinkansen lines, which were paid by JR-West, JR-Central, and JR-East to the Development Fund. The final 20% of the new line's cost was dealt with in the form of a long-term loan, which the operating companies paid once the route had come into operation. The charges reflect the difference between operating costs before and after the change-over.

On the occasion of the writer's visit, our party had an excellent lunch in the *teppanyaki* restaurant at the new station hotel at Yamagata itself, and then travelled on to Tendo, on the Japanese gauge, in a three-car class 701 EMU. This clearly had three-phase motors, as its traction system played us a tune each time we accelerated! It was also interesting to watch the driver in action, pointing to the various gauges, controls and lineside signals at the appropriate times, in the approved way to maintain full personal vigilance. On our return to Yamagata we were also encouraged to get a print off the large 'do-it-yourself' station-identification rubber-stamp. Making a collection of these used to be a great pastime for young passengers.

The popularity of the Yamagata gauge conversion has been so great that the 'Mini-Shinkansen' services have since been extended a further 61.5 km (38.2 miles) to Shinjo, the new line coming into service at the end of 1999, after the gauge-conversion team had relaid up to 2 km of track in a single day. JR-East constructed two 7-car Series E3 sets for this extension, to supplement the existing 12 Series 40s. As a result, by the year 2000, trains had replaced all but one of the daily scheduled flights between Yamagata and Tokyo.

There may, however, be less of these track conversions in future, as work has begun at the Railway Technical Institute on 'flexible-gauge' trains, the prototype for which is currently under test in the United States. For several years now the Spanish Talgos have run through between the standard-gauge AVE tracks and the rest of that country's 'Iberian-gauge' lines, but each of their wheels is carried on a separate axle, which is rather different from the normal railway system. Potential sites for several strategic gauge-changing sites have already been pin-pointed in Japan.

Back in the 1990s, the success of the Yamagata conversion, not surprisingly, prompted a start on another such scheme, this time to link Morioka, at the north end of the Tohoku Shinkansen, with Akita on the west coast of Honshu, using 127 km (79 miles) of gauge-converted line. From Morioka to Omagari the 75.6 km (47.0 miles) of the Tazawako Line are single track, and have had the gauge widened throughout. At Omagari it joins the Ou line for the remaining 51.7 km (32.1 miles) to Akita. Some of this stretch is double track, and only one of these has had its gauge changed. On the remainder there is a mixed-gauge track to permit the passage of freight trains, and through passenger services to those lines retaining the '1067mm-gauge'.

Work on the conversion began in 1992, and the line was formally opened in March 1997. The Series E3 train-sets used on it resemble the Series 400s, but there are a number of differences. Light-alloy bodies keep the maximum axle-load down to 12 tonnes rather than the previous 13, and VVVF-powered three-phase traction motors are provided. The five-car trains include a trailer, so their installed power is 4.8 MW (6435 h.p.), with the same ability to run on the two different voltages as the Series 400s. Wheelchair access and spaces are provided, and the end walls of the cars are appropriately panelled in Akita cedar. To house all the electrical equipment, the roof is domed slightly in cross-section which makes the vehicles 110mm (4¼ins) higher than the first 'Mini-Shinkansen' ones. An unusual feature is the 25/20 kV train-line running along the length of the train *between* the roof and the ceiling of the saloons.

The fastest Tokyo–Akita service used to take 4hr 28min, inclusive of the change of trains, but, because of curvature restrictions on the branch, the fastest time by through 'Mini-Shinkansen' running at the previous maximum speed would only be cut to 4hr, which would still not have been competitive with the airlines. The trains have therefore been given a 275 km/h (171 m.p.h.) capability for the main line, but, to get permission to run at this speed, there had to be no environmental deterioration between Morioka and Tokyo. The design of the E3 sets had to ensure that this was achieved in spite of the speed-up. As it was not acceptable to operate Series 200 sets at this speed on the Tohoku Shinkansen, the fastest Akita expresses consist of an E3 set coupled to one of the new E2, full-sized, Shinkansen units. Details of these two new designs of train are given later in this chapter.

Additional work has also begun on the Hokuriku Shinkansen route in JR-East territory, which will eventually run from Takasaski, on the Joetsu line, north-westwards through Nagano to reach the coast of the Sea of Japan. After serving the major cities there, it will cross Honshu again to terminate at Osaka. While one presumes there will be through trains between Tokyo and Osaka, the much greater journey distance will prevent it becoming a competitor to the original Tokaido Line, although the links between the north coast and those two cities will be invaluable.

The first 117.4 km (72.9 miles) of this route, from Takasaki to Nagano, were opened as the Nagano Shinkansen in time to provide better services for the 1998 Winter Olympics, which were held close to that city, when no less 655 000 people travelled to the Olympic events by Shinkansen. This was by no means a 'one-off' surge, as in 1998 business on the Nagano line increased by 30%, helped by the construction of a 1000-space car park at the out-of-city station. As a result the Minister of Transport authorised the construction of the next stretch of the Hokuriku line to full Shinkansen standards in March 1998. This will take it as far as the city of Joetsu, near the coast north of Nagano, sometimes causing confusion between that city and the much older Joetsu Shinkansen, the origins of the names being totally different!

To reduce the construction costs, the new Nagano line is steeply-graded, with more than 30 km (18½ miles) between Takasaki and Karuizawa being inclined at 3% (1 in 33), so regenerative braking is used to ensure stable braking performance. There is another electrical complication too, as the line crosses the 'Frequency Divide' between the country's 50 and 60 Hz systems. When the Tokaido Shinkansen was built in the 1960s, the stretch in 50 Hz-territory was provided with frequency-converters at the feeder stations. Thirty years on it is now feasible to equip the trains to run on both systems, and this has been done. Modern a.c. traction motors have their three-phase VVVF power supplies generated from an intermediate d.c. link, so the task is not as difficult as it would have been with the original d.c. motors. This system can easily be used 'backwards' to provide regenerative braking, and will hold the Series E2s at 210 km/h (130 m.p.h.) on the 1 in 33 descent without the use of the disc brakes, which are capable of bringing the train to a stop by themselves if required.

The Series E2 sets are used on the Nagano Shinkansen, and their installed power is 7.2 MW (9650 h.p.). Although capable of running at 275 km/h on the Tohoku Shinkansen, as mentioned earlier, they will be limited to 260 km/h (162 m.p.h.) on the line to Nagano. The fastest times from Tokyo were cut from 2hr 50 mins to 1hr 30 min when the new line opened in 1997. It was to handle all these extra northern Shinkansen trains that the additional platforms were built at Tokyo Central.

Work has also started on several new Shinkansen lines in JR-East territory, the details of all of them being as follows:

	_km_	_Miles_	_Work started_
HOKURIKU SHINKANSEN			
Nagano–Joetsu	60	37	1998
Itoigawa–Uozu	40	25	1993
Isurugi–Kanazawa	25	16	1992
TOHOKU SHINKANSEN			
Morioka–Hachinohe	97	60	1991
Hachinohe–Shin-Aomori	82	51	1998

No mention has so far been made of the first extension to the East Japan Shinkansen system after Privatisation. This was a very simple one, the idea for which had actually been proposed by a group of seven permanent-way employees in JNR days, but it could not be taken forward until after the split. It involved building a new station alongside the track-maintenance depot at Gala Yuzawa, which is sited at the end of a 1.8 km (1.1 mile) branch from Echigo-Yuzawa on the Joetsu Shinkansen. This is in the centre of a winter-sports area, and a cableway with its base station alongside the railway provides an easy link with the ski slopes on Mount Takatsukura. Since 1990, seasonal trains have run direct from Tokyo to Gala Yuzawa in 80 minutes.

As mentioned earlier, after Privatisation the original Shinkansen lines were sold to the three large Honshu railway companies, but these new extensions are being built by the government agency, Japanese Railway Construction Public Corporation, which will lease them to the private railway

companies after completion. All told 513 km (319 miles) of new Shinkansen lines are currently under construction. Some of the '1067mm-gauge' lines replaced by the new Shinkansen routes are being offered to private companies.

It will be seen that the JR-East's Shinkansen have developed into a network, which makes it very different type of system compared with the linear Tokaido-Sanyo line operated by JR-Central and JR-West. Although the eastern end of the Hokuriku Shinkansen does have trains running to and from Tokyo, when the lengthy stretch along the Sea of Japan is is completed, it will effectively be centred on Osaka, rather than the country's capital.

Having described the development of JR-East's Shinkansen, we will now look at how their operations have altered. Table 9.1 shows the changes that have taken place in the ridership on the Tohoku and Joetsu Shinkansen since Privatisation. Included in the figures for the former are those for the Yamagata 'Mini-Shinkansen'.

Tohoku and Joetsu Shinkansen Rolling-Stock since Privatisation

In Chapter 6 we left our consideration of the rolling-stock developments on the Tohoku and Joetsu Shinkansen just before Privatisation in 1987, and will now pick up the story to bring it up to date. At that time the numbers of long-distance travellers were increasing by 8–13% annually, but the slower, all-stations, _Aoba_ and _Toki_ services were losing passengers.

In 1986 four new cars with driving cabs had been purchased, to enable more, shorter, sets to be formed, using the existing stock of intermediate cars. The reformed units consisted of ten rather than the usual 12 vehicles, and were known as the G-fleet. It subsequently turned out that these still provided more accommodation than needed on the stopping services, and they were further shortened to eight cars. Some of the vehicles displaced by this move were also provided with cabs, enabling the number of 240 km/h F-fleet sets to be increased to cover the rise in long-distance passengers. Over the years that followed, more of the E-fleet sets were shortened and given cars modified with driving cabs, and the G-fleet finally increased to 18 during 1990, as shown in Table 9.2.

The first 'new-image' Series 100 set had been built for the Tokaido Shinkansen in 1985, and entered passenger service in October that year. When the four new driving cars were built for the Tohoku and Joetsu Shinkansen in 1986, it was no surprise that their cabs had the new pro-

	Table 9.1							
	Tohoku, Joetsu & Nagano Shinkansen Passenger Loadings 1986–1999							
	Tohoku Shinkansen		**Joetsu Shinkansen**		**Nagano Shinkansen**		**Total**	
Year	Passengers (million)	Passenger-km (billion)	Passengers (million)	Passenger-km (billion)	Passengers (million)	Passenger-km (billion)	Passengers (million)	Passenger-km (billion)
1986/87	32.0	8.2	16.0	3.4	-	-	48.0	11.6
1987/88	45.2	8.9	16.8	3.2	-	-	62.0	12.1
1988/89	49.1	9.7	18.9	3.6	-	-	68.0	13.3
1989/90	51.5	9.9	19.8	3.7	-	-	71.3	13.6
1990/91	57.7	10.7	22.8	4.1	-	-	80.5	14.8
1991/92	65.7	11.7	25.9	4.4	-	-	91.6	16.1
1992/93	68.4	11.8	26.7	4.4	-	-	95.1	16.2
1993/94	68.6	11.7	26.6	4.3	-	-	95.2	16.0
1994/95	69.5	11.8	26.6	4.3	-	-	96.1	16.1
1995/96	71.7	12.0	27.3	4.3	-	-	99.0	16.3
1996/97	74.0	12.2	28.0	4.4	-	-	102.0	16.6
1997/98	76.8	12.3	32.1	4.4	5.1	4.7	114.0	21.4
1998/99	79.0	12.1	35.6	4.6	9.1	8.0	123.7	24.7
Source: JR-E								

Above: Railway Technical Research Institute's 'Flexible-Gauge' train, currently on test in the United States.   *Railway Technical Research Institute*

Right: "A-bout turn". A sequence showing the automatic reversal of blocks of non-reserved seats in one of JR-East's MAX double-deck Shinkansen.
      JR-East

Below: Diagrams showing how gauge is changed from 1067mm (1) to standard-gauge (4) as experimental unit traverses a special section of track. As the axle extensions ride on to the special roller-tracks (2) the wheels are allowed to drop slightly, freeing the locking device on tops of the axleboxes. The guide rails then push the wheels to their new position (3), after which the roller-tracks rise to lock the wheels in their new position.
      Railway Technical Research Institute

1.

Wheels are locked during regular travel.

軸箱   狭軌   軸箱

2.

Approach section

Axleboxes ride on support rails. As wheelsets descend, locking pins disengage.

軸箱支持レール

3.

Gauge changing

Guide rails push wheels to new positions.

案内レール

4.

As wheels rise again, locking pins re-engage at new position.

ロック   ロック

標準軌

Above: The 'shoulders' behind the cab of the Series E2 sets are very apparent in this view of an E2' coupled to an E3 during a trial run at Omiya in early 1996.
Mikio Miura

Right: A prototype Series E2' (right) undergoing trials with a Series E3. *JR-East*

Below: One of JR-East's *MAX* double-deck Shinkansen. *Mikio Miura*

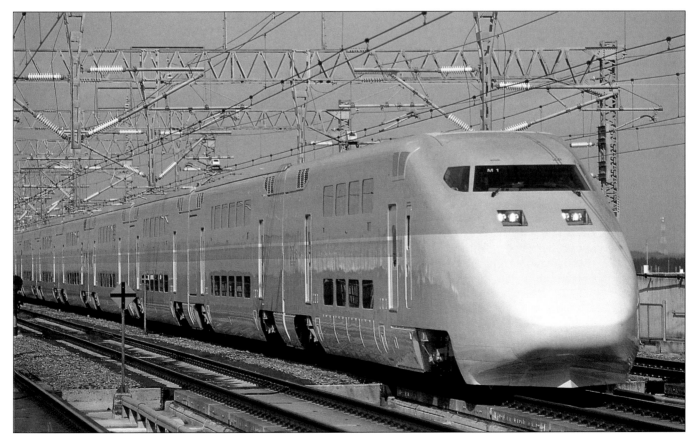

Table 9.2
Tohoku, Joetsu & Nagano Shinkansen Train-sets 198–2000

Fleet Letter	Date Introduced	Series	No. of Cars	Set Composition	Comments
E	1980	200	12	12M	Original light-alloy Series 200 trains.
F	1983	200	12	12M	As E-fleet but with maximum speed raised to 240 km/h. Four sets modified in 1989 to run at up to 275km/h.
G	1987	200	10	10M	Shortened sets without bar service for *Aoba* and *Toki* services.
H	1990	200	16	14M2T	Bi-level trailer cars introduced. Some sets ran with 13 cars from June 1990 to June 1991.
K	1991	200	8	8M	Sets with automatic couplings to work with Series 400 (L-fleet) trains between Tokyo and Fukushima. Maximum speed 240 km/h.
L	1990/1999	400/E3	6/7	5M1T/5M2T	'Mini-Shinkansen' for through services to Yamagata. Later provided with an additional trailer in the set. Most of L-fleet are Series 400s, but two sets were formed from Series E3 in 1998.
M	1993	E1	12	6M6T	Full double-deck Shinkansen trains, known as MAX.
J	1995	E2	8	6M2T	Sets used on Tohoku Shinkansen, with automatic couplings to work with Series E3.
N	1995	E2	8	6M2T	Sets used on the Nagano Shikankansen, without automatic couplings.
R	1995	E3	6	4M2T	Mini-Shinkansen for through services to Akita. Later provided with an additional trailer in the set.
P	1997	E4	8	4M4T	Second design of full double-deck Shinkansen trains, known as 'New MAX'. A train of two sets will seat no less than 1,634 people, the world's largest total of passengers for a high-speed train.

Year	Cars New	Cars Total	E	F	G	H	K	L	M	J	N	R	P	Total	Comments
3/1987	-	684	20	29	10	-	-	-	-	-	-	-	-	59	Totals at privatisation.
1987	-	684	19	33	8	-	-	-	-	-	-	-	-	60	-
1988	-	684	18	34	8	-	-	-	-	-	-	-	-	60	-
1989	6	690	13	34	15	-	-	-	-	-	-	-	-	62	New double-deck cars for *Yamabiko* services
1990	12	698	10	28	18	6	-	-	-	-	-	-	-	62	New double-deck cars for *Yamabiko* services.
1991	-	698	5	26	18	6	11	1	-	-	-	-	-	67	Services extended into Tokyo Central station.
1992	66	772	-	31	18	6	11	12	-	-	-	-	-	78	Additional series 400 sets for services to Yamagata.
1993	-	772	-	31	18	6	11	12	2	-	-	-	-	80	-
1994	24	808	-	31	18	6	11	12	3	-	-	-	-	81	First two double-deck MAX sets.
1995	81	848	-	31	18	6	11	12	6	-	-	-	-	84	Prototype Series E2 and E3. Trailer added to each L-set.
1996	63	960	-	20	17	6	22	12	6	4	-	16	-	103	Additional Series E2 and E3 sets.
1997	172	1 080	-	20	14	6	22	12	6	6	13	16	3	118	Services extended to Nagano. 'New MAX' sets built
1998	78	1 110	-	20	8	6	22	12	6	10	13	17	6	120	Series E4 and additional E2 sets. Trailer added to each R set
1999	86	1 102	-	20	-	6	19	14	6	15	13	17	10	120	Additional Series E2 and E4 sets. Two series E3 constructed for Yamagata service

Source: JR-E

file, making them Series 100 'look-alike', known officially as Series 200-2000. The same design, with its flamboyantly shaped snow-plough, was used when some of the surplus vehicles from the G-fleet were also fitted with cabs.

In 1990, more capacity was needed to accommodate the long-distance business, and 12 new bi-level trailers were purchased for the *Yamabiko* sets, the resulting six units being classified as H-fleet. These were the first non-powered vehicles on the northern high-speed lines, but experience showed the stretched sets with their 16 cars were easily able to maintain the schedules. While all these changes were taking place, some sets had to run with only 13 cars until June 1991. To match the more modern image, the driving cars with the new profile were allocated to these trains. Each of these bi-level vehicles has Green Car seating on the upper level. Half of them provide a number of small compartments on the lower level, one for ordinary passengers and the rest for Green Car ticket-holders, while the others have a cafeteria and bar. A 'lifter' is provided to enable wheelchair passengers bypass the stairs.

While all these changes were taking place, four of the F-fleet sets were modified in 1989 to operate at 275 km/h (171 m.p.h.). This was a bit of 'one-up-manship' to enable East Japan Railway to keep ahead of the other two high-speed lines which were starting to publicise their plans for the Series 300 (*Nozomi*) services which were actually launched in 1992. These modified JR-East F-fleet sets re-quired a new signalling system and only operate on the Joetsu route. From March 1990 two northbound *Super Asahi* trains daily were permitted to run at the higher speed on the northern end of the line, over the 62 km (38½ miles) between Jomo Kogen and Urasa. The maximum time saving was no more than two minutes, but in the new privatised regime there are clearly public-relations advantages for East Japan Railway to maintain its position as the operator of the country's fastest trains. That still applied, even after the other two Honshu companies introduced their Series 300 *Nozomi* services in 1993, running every hour between Tokyo and Hakata, and covering long distances at 270 km/h – a mere 5 km/h (3 m.p.h.) slower. The situation changed, however, when the Series 500s begin operating at 300km/h on the Sanyo Shinkansen in 1997.

STAR 21

In the 1990s all three Honshu-based JR companies built experimental Shinkansen trains to investigate the possibilities of yet higher running speeds. East Japan Railway's unit was STAR 21 (**S**uperior **T**rain for the **A**dvanced **R**ailway toward the **21**st century), and provided much vital data for the design of subsequent commercial units.

This experimental train was delivered in March 1992, and consisted of nine cars, marshalled in two distinct 'halves'. The Type 952 half-set had four separate vehicles, but the other five Type 953 cars were articulated throughout. This was the first time such a system had been used on

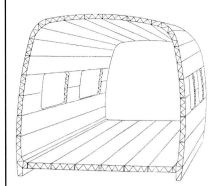

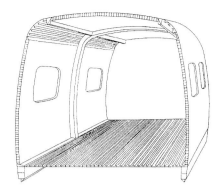

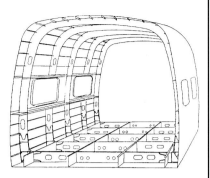

Diagrams showing the three different methods of body construction used with STAR 21. © *East Japan Railway Company*

Welded hollow light-alloy sections. Brazed alumimium honeycomb sheet. Duralumin aircraft-type structure.

a Japanese high-speed train, although it has always been a feature of the French TGVs. It is not all that easy to identify which 'half' of the set one was looking at, because the bogies were completely covered by fairings in the interests of noise-suppression. This may be why the two sections were painted in slightly different liveries, the articulated coaches being very pale green and the others off-white. Bands of jade-green covered the window areas, edged with narrow white stripes top and bottom.

The front-ends of the two driving vehicles were also slightly different, but both had generally-similar wedge-shaped profiles with very little lateral taper, and most of the difference was in the detailed treatment of windows, lights, etc. Within the unit, however, there are many more variations. Three separate construction methods were used for the coach bodies. There were three different types of primary suspension for the axles, and two forms of articulation were been tried out. STAR 21's cars were 200 mm (4 in) lower than those of the new Series E2s, and 150 mm (3 in) lower than the cars on a Series 300. They were also 11 in (280 mm) narrower than both these other designs.

To deal with the bodies first, three of the individual vehicles were constructed by longitudinally welding together hollow light-alloy sections, in the same general way as was done for BR's APT-P. On STAR 21 the external surfaces were 1.9mm thick, but the central floor beams were thinner, at 1.5mm. The world's largest press was used to manufacture the basic extrusions, using a force of 90 000 kN. The two cars either side of the central 'divide' were built from

brazed aluminium honeycomb sheet, 30mm (just under 1¼ in) thick. The outer surfaces were formed from an 0.8 mm aluminum alloy sheet on the interior side, while a 1.0 mm one was used on the outside of the coach. Brazed between them was a honeycomb made of 0.2 mm sheet. The resulting coach body, with its ribs and longerons, was light, rigid, and had good airtight properties. On STAR 21 these two coaches had circular windows, but production vehicles would have had the usual rectangular type. STAR 21's remaining four articulated cars were manufactured like the body of a traditional aircraft, with a framework of duralumin covered by a thin skin of the same material. Between 130 000 and 150 000 rivets were needed per coach.

All the bolsterless bogies had a wheelbase of 2500 mm (8ft 8in), and were tested for stability at speeds of over 500 km/h on a roller-rig. By using high-tensile steel for the frames, and fitting hollow axles, small-diameter wheels, and very light traction-motors, the combined weight of all 14 bogies on the train was only 82.4 tonnes. By comparison, the 16 fitted to an eight-car Series 200 set weighed a total of 135.4 tonnes. The 330 kW (440 h.p.) three-phase asynchronous traction motors turned the scales at 330 kg (737 lb) each, so had a specific weight of unity (1 kg/kW). By contrast, those on the Series 200 and Series 400 ('Mini-Shinkansen') trains have ratios of 4.0 and 3.3 kg/kW, respectively, showing how technology has changed since the 1980s. In all, eight different types of bogie were used, with three alternative designs for the axlebox primary suspensions.

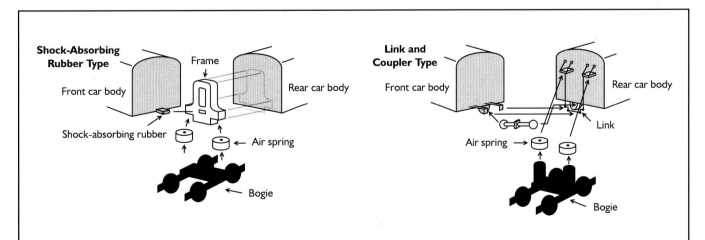

The two different articulated suspension systems on STAR 21, using (left) shock-absorbing rubber, and (right) the link-and-coupler. © *East Japan Railway Company*

73

Above: A JR-East E3 *Komachi* with Mount Iwate in the background.   *Mikio Miura*

Below: A JR-East *Komachi* crosses the Tama River.   *Mikio Miura*

Top: E4 Max logo. *Mikio Miura*

Above: Nagano Shinkansen logo on Series E2 Shinkansen. *Mikio Miura*

Right: A JR-East Series E2 on a *Asama* train crosses Chikkumagawa Viaduct on the Nagano Shinkansen in October 1997. *Mikio Miura*

Below: JR-East's STAR 21 experimental train which set several Japanese railway speed records in 1992/3. The change in the shape of the bogie fairings indicates the two different halves of the set. *JR-East*

Two different articulation systems were tested on the Type 953 set. In one of them, the air-springs supported the bottom of a car-body frame, attached to one end of the bodyshell. The end of the adjacent car carried a lug which was inserted into a slot in the frame, with an elastomer joint to permit limited relative movement. With the alternative arrangement, the air springs were mounted high up on pillars, as with the TGVs, and the car was supported from a pair of brackets built out from the end of the car. The other car was suspended from the first by a horizontal, low-level link, the centre of which was carried by a spherical bearing on the bogie.

Star 21 was also provided with two different power systems. The first was the more usual arrangement, with the variable-frequency, three-phase, supply being generated in a motor-block which powered all four motors on a particular car. The other arrangement had smaller, separate, inverters for each traction motor, which enabled full power to be produced even if there were differences in the wheel diameters. (The power output of an asynchronous motor is determined by the ratio of its rotational speed to the frequency of the supply. The nearer the two are to being in synchronisation, the less power is generated, so a difference in power output can occur if more than one axle is powered by the same inverter).

Originally STAR 21's Type 953 unit had a 330 kW motor on each axle of the articulated bogies, but the outer ordinary ones were unpowered. On the Type 952 unit four of its eight bogies were motored. There were thus eight powered bogies on the train, giving a total of 5280 kW (7075 h.p.), but its power was subsequently up-rated, as described later. None of the French TGVs or their variants have been built with articulated bogies that are powered. With most types, the only motorised bogies are the 'ordinary' ones on the power cars, although on some trains, like the Eurostars, the outer bogie on the adjacent passenger vehicle is also fitted with motors to provide sufficient overall power. The TGV design also has the traction motors fixed to the underside of the vehicle's floor, rather than to the bogie frame, which requires a more complicated drivetrain. The overall weight of STAR 21 in its original form was 265.6 tonnes, so the power:weight ratio worked out at 14.9kW/tonne (19.7 h.p./ton), the same as that of a 16-car Series 200 train.

Although STAR 21 was an experimental train, and much of its interior was therefore filled with recording equipment, five different types of super-lightweight seating were installed. All of them reclined, and the blocks rotated in the usual way to enable passengers to face the direction of travel. Individual seats only weighed 18.6 kg (41 lb). In view of the slightly reduced coach-width compared with the Series 200s, the planned layout had a 2+2 arrangement in the ordinary coaches and 2+1 in the Green Car. During the trials, various different interior treatments were tried out to improve the ambience and comfort. Special toilets for wheelchair passengers were also tested.

Fully-fitted out with seats, STAR 21 would have weighed only just over half as much per passenger as a Series 200 train, which is another indication of how technology had improved in little more than a decade. Table 9.3 gives a more detailed comparison of the weights of the two experimental half-sets and the Series 200. Overall it will be seen that the nine-car (952 + 953) weighed only 15 tonnes more than four cars of the earlier design. As a result, the Type 952 unit had an average empty axle-load of no more than 7.6 tonnes, while the articulated Type 953 was, surprisingly, higher at 9.7 tonnes. Both are remarkable figures when compared with contemporary European high-speed trains.

The ink in the record books was barely dry after West Japan's WIN350 had achieved its design speed in August 1992, as described in the next chapter, when STAR 21 started to steal the limelight, as shown in Table 10.2. Running on the Joetsu Shinkansen it reached 353.0 km/h (219.3 m.p.h.) on 30 October 1992, capturing the Japanese rail speed record, and then pushed this up to

358.0 km/h (222.5 m.p.h.) the following day. There was then a gap of nearly a year until 15 September 1993 before the first of four new records was established. During the interim STAR 21 was modified by having more of its axles motored, increasing its overall rating to 7920 kW (10615 h.p.). With the aid of this boost, on 13 December 1993 it passed the 400 km/h mark, and then achieved 425.0 (264.1 m.p.h.) eight days later. This put it ahead of any other train in the world except the SNCF's heavily modified TGV-Atlantique set No. 325, which had reached 515.3 km/h (320.2 m.p.h.) in May 1990.

East Japan Railway were naturally delighted with this achievement as well as all the experimental data obtained during the many test runs with STAR 21. Although few obvious external features from STAR 21 appear in the new generation Series E2s and E3s referred to in this chapter, their detailed design will undoubtedly have benefited from the experiences with the record-breaker. One of the end cars of JR-East's STAR21, together with a similar vehicle from JR-West's WIN350, (described in the next chapter) has been preserved at the Japanese Railway Technical Centre in Maibara.

Earlier in this chapter, the use of the Series 400 'Mini-Shinkansen' sets for the Yamagata line was described. The prototype was delivered in 1991, and the remaining 11 L-fleet sets were built the following year. At this stage they consisted of six cars only, but an additional, unpowered, vehicle was added to each in 1994 to match the rising demand for seats. To work with these 'Mini-Shinkansen', 11 K-fleet sets were introduced in 1991. These are eight-car trains, with an automatic coupling on the outer end of the northern driving vehicle, to enable them to work with the Series 400 units between Tokyo and Fukushima. They were formed from the last five of the original E-fleet trains, plus two of the F-fleet units, with another eight intermediate cars being fitted with driving cabs. Although the E-fleet sets had been restricted to 220 km/h (137 m.p.h.), in their new guise they were all capable of running at 240 km/h (149 m.p.h.), to match the main-line capabilities of the Series 400s. From then on the whole of the East Japan Shinkansen fleet, with the exception of the G-fleet, could travel at 240 km/h or faster.

The year 1993 saw East Japan Railway taking delivery of the world's first fully double-deck high-speed train, the Series E1. Each of the cars on these massive 12-car sets has passenger saloons at both levels, and provides a grand total for the train of 1235 seats. (There are additionally tip-up seats in some of the vestibules). Even the much-vaunted SNCF TGV-Duplex sets do not have passenger accommodation in the end driving vehicles, the body-space of which is fully occupied with the train's power-supply equipment. The engineering difficulties to be overcome at the design stage were immense, and, although their bodies are of steel construction, the maximum axle-load is 17 tonnes, the same as that for French TGVs.

The trains have been marketed as MAX (**M**ulti **A**menity E**x**press), another interesting example of the Japanese use of the English language as the basis for acronyms. Amenities of various different sorts are provided, the main one being the additional seating space available at peak travelling times. The non-reserved ordinary seating provided in the upper level of the four cars at one end of the train are in the 3+3 arrangement, rather than the usual Shinkansen 3+2. The argument is that

	Table 9.3 **Weight Comparisons between STAR 21 and Series 200 Shinkansen**		
	Series 200	Type 952	Type 953
No. of cars	4	4	5
Weights (tonnes)			
Passenger load	18.5	13.5	14.7
Bogies	67.7	44.9	37.5
Traction equipment	33.4	10.0	9.7
Car bodies	84.6	44.4	46.4
Other items	46.5	21.7	22.8
TOTALS	**250.7**	**134.5**	**131.1**
Average axle-load			
Empty	14.5	7.6	9.7
Full	15.7	8.4	10.9
Source: JR-E			

Table 9.4
Tohoku & Joetsu Shinkansen Train Specifications

Series	200	400	E1	E2	E3	E4
Composition	12M (8M,14M2T)	6M1T	6M6T	6M2T	4M1T	4M4T
Seats						
Ordinary	833	379	1133	579	247	763
Green Car	52	20	102	51	23	54
Weight Empty (tonnes)	697	318	692	366	220	428
Body						
Construction	Light alloy	Steel	Light alloy	Light alloy	Light alloy	Light alloy
Dimensions (mm/ft)						
Width	3 380/11.1	2 947/ 9.7	3 380/11.1	3 380/11.1	2 945/9.7	3 380/11.1
Length	25 000/82.0	20 000/65.6	25 000/82.0	25 000/82.0	20 000/65.6	25 000/82.0
Height	4 000/13.1	3 970/13.0	4 485/14.7	3 700/12.1	4 080/13.4	4 485/14.7
Bogies						
Type	Bolster	Bolsterless	Bolsterless	Bolsterless	Bolsterless	Bolsterless
Wheelbase (mm/ft)	2500/8.2	2250/7.4	2500/8.2	2500/8.2	2250/7.4	2500/8.2
Wheel dia. (mm/in)	910/35.8	860/33.9	910/35.8	860/33.9	860/33.9	910/35.8
Braking						
Motored	Rheostatic	Rheostatic	Regen.	Regenerative	Regenerative	Regenerative
Trailer	Disc	Disc	Disc	Disc	Disc	Disc
Traction motors						
Type	d.c.	d.c.	VVVF	VVVF	VVVF	VVVF
Power (kw/h.p.)	230/310	210/280	410/550	300/400	300/400	420/560
Train total (MW/h.p.)	11.0/14 800	5.0/6760	9.8/13 190	7.2/9650	4.8/6430	6.7/9100
Max. speed (km/h/m.p.h.)	210-275/130-171	240/149	240/149	275/171	275/171	240/149
Max. axle-load (tonnes) (fully loaded)	17.0	13.0	17.0	13.0	12.0	16.0

Source: JR-E

those without seat reservations would prefer to have somewhere to sit down, even if the space is not quite as wide as usual. The centre of the middle seat-back in each such block folds down to provide a shelf/armrest when the train is not full.

The coaches are the same width as ordinary Shinkansen stock, but their roof-line is nearly half a metre higher above the track. The units' general specifications are given in Table 9.4, along with those for the other East Japan trains introduced since 1987. Clever design was again necessary to fit two saloons into just over a foot and a half of extra height. However it was inevitable that the windows of the lower saloons would be below the level of the lineside noise walls, so anyone wanting to see the countryside has to travel in the upper saloons. With the exception of those in the non-reserved sections, the seats recline, and all of them are capable of undergoing even more complicated move-

ments. When a train reaches the end of its journey and passengers have alighted, the press of one of the buttons situated in the driver's cab, and at each end of every car, causes every seat block in the whole train to rotate. The next load of passengers can then start their journey facing the direction of travel.

A lot of other amenities are provided in these trains. Vending-machines have been installed in three different coaches, two of which can dispense lunch-boxes. There is also a drinks bar in Car No. 8. Lifts take wheelchair passengers to the upper decks of one of the ordinary cars and the adjacent Green Car. To assist those able to transfer from their mobile seats, moveable side-arms are provided on certain of the train seats to facilitate the task. All toilets are 'Western style', and, for the first time on a Shinkansen, a 'Ladies Only' one is provided. There is also a 'Powder Room' which provides space for making-up and changing, as well as feeding babies and changing their nappies.

The Series E1 trains have equal numbers of power cars and trailers, so there are, *in toto*, 24 traction motors, each of 410 kW (550 h.p.). They are of three-phase design, powered by a VVVF system with full regenerative braking. Maximum speed is 240 km/h (149 m.p.h.). It is an interesting thought that the extremely safety-conscious Japanese railways have no qualms about as many as 86 passengers riding in the leading vehicle at such a speed, but their lines are better protected from straying cattle than was that between Edinburgh and Glasgow, where the fatal derailment at Polmont was caused by a cow. The UK Railway Inspectorate has not so far permitted any passengers to travel in the leading vehicle of a train that runs at more than 100 m.p.h. (160 km/h), but, at the time of writing, Virgin Trains are building 140 m.p.h. sets designed to carry passengers in the leading cars.

Table 9.5
Tohoku & Joetsu Shinkansen Train Services 1986–1994
(Basic numbers of trains per day)

	Tohoku Shinkansen				Joetsu Shinkansen			Grand
Year	*Yamabiko*	*Aoba*	*Tsubasa*	Total	*Asahi*	*Toki*	Total	Total
1986*	58	36	-	94	34	31	65	159
1988	76	41	-	117	36	47	83	200
1989	76	42	-	118	36	48	84	202
1990	76	42	-	118	36	49	85	203
1991	76	42	-	118	38	48	86	204
1993	80	42	28†	124	38	48	86	210
1994	83	44	28†	129	39	50	89	218

* Timetable change in 1986 was in November. All others in March.
† Most *Tsubasa* trains run coupled with a *Yamabiko* service between Tokyo and Fukushima. Only those which operate independently between Tokyo and Fukushima are included in the total columns.

Source: JR-E

Each axle on the MAX trailers is provided with disc brakes, and throughout the train the brake force is related to the loads on each bogie by means of sensors measuring the air-bag internal pressures. Fully-loaded there are likely to be over 80 tons of passengers aboard, representing 11% of the train's empty weight, so the need for such equipment is obvious. Bolsterless bogies are provided, with the usual weight-saving features like hollow axles and aluminum-alloy traction-motor gearboxes.

A completely new livery was adopted for these trains. The bottom half of their bodywork is painted white, with the upper half finished in a medium blue-grey. There is a broad jade-green horizontal band along the sides of each coach, edged with the roof colour. This colour-scheme became sufficiently popular for TomixClub to bring out a wrist-watch with the face, as well as the strap, in the two colours. The driving cabs have a wide, unobstructed windscreen, which gives very good visibility, and there is also a Crew Room. This resembles the Train Captain's 'office' on the Eurotunnel Lorry Shuttles, being provided with monitors and other equipment for checking the cars. Four high-power headlights are mounted in side-by-side pairs below the windscreen.

Left: A JR-East MAX crosses one of the main roads in Tokyo city centre.
Mikio Miura

Below: A 1996 line-up of JR-East's Shinkansen sets. Left to right - 'Doctor Yellow', Series 400, Series 200-2000, STAR 21, MAX (Series E1), prototype Series E2 and prototype Series E3.
JR-East

By 1995 there were six MAX sets in service, and a typical roster for one of them was as follows:

Sendai Depot	dep.	06.15
Sendai station	dep.	06.42
Tokyo Central	arr.	09.08
	dep.	09.12
Ueno Depot	arr.	09.18
	dep.	09.45
Tokyo Central	arr.	09.51
	dep.	09.57
Morioka	arr.	13.34
	dep.	15.00
Tokyo Central	arr.	18.28
	dep.	18.40
Nasu-Shiobara	arr.	19.52
	dep	20.37
Tokyo Central	arr.	21.52
	dep.	21.56
Ueno Depot	arr.	22.08

Above right: The inaugural ceremony for the first JR-East E3 *Komachi* at Tokyo Central on 22 March 1997.

Right: The interior of the upper level of Car No.8 in a JR-East E4 Max, showing the moveable seat for wheel-chair passengers. A lift is available to take them up from platform level. *Mikio Miura (2)*

New Liveries for JR-East Shinkansen

Below left: Series E3 *Tsubasa* in the new livery adopted for the extension to Shinjo.

Below right: Four birds fly across the full moon – the logo of a tourism campaign sponsored by the area served by the Series E3 trains.

Bottom left: New logo for Series E3 trains.

Bottom right: The new livery adopted for the refurbished Series 200 sets which started to enter service in February 1999. They also have new curved windscreens, and improved seating. *Mikio Miura (4)*

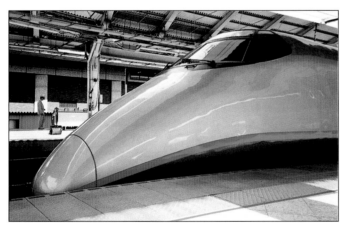

The total distance travelled in the day was 1633.6 km or 1015 miles, which exceeds the length of most daily TGV rosters, although those for some of the UK East Coast HSTs and Intercity 225s have equalled it. It will be noted that, like many UK Intercity sets, a cyclic system is worked, with the set at the end of the day not returning to the same depot from which it started. As described in an earlier chapter, Sendai is the maintenance works for the rolling-stock on both the Tohoku and Joetsu Shinkansen, and the site also includes a servicing depot. Elsewhere on the two systems, servicing is carried out in the depots at Ueno, Marioka and Niigata.

Table 9.5 shows how the number of regular daily train services on the Tohoku and Joetsu Shinkansen increased between Privatisation and 1994. It will be seen that an overall increase of a quarter took place at the first timetable change after Privatisation, but the figure then remained fairly constant before rising again by another 5% with the start of the Shinkansen services to Yamagata. (In this table, only the one train a day on the branch in each direction which runs through without attaching or detaching a Sendai portion at Fukushima is included in the total.)

More recently, however, the services out of Tokyo Central have been considerably recast to deal with the marked increase in travel to and from the commuter belt, which now stretches out as far as Nasu-Shiobara. This is the next station north of Utsunomiya, and is 157.8 km (98.1 miles) from Tokyo Central, so, from a distance point of view, roughly corresponds with Grantham relative to London by the East Coast route. As shown in Table 9.6 there are 15 *Nasumo* services a day going no further north than this station, the name being derived from the nearby recreational area. All trains worked by these double-deckers are now specifically referred to in the timetables,

and they are used on all types of train except those involved with the Yamagata services. In the ski season, these sets are even rostered for specials to Gala Yuzawa. This table differs from Table 9.5 in that all the Yamagata and Akita workings are included in the totals, but, if the 26 *Tsubasa* which run coupled with *Yamabiko* workings, and the corresponding 28 *Komanchi* services are deducted, the grand total still comes to 309 trains/day, which is appreciably up on the 1994 figure, and higher than the 229 running daily in 1996. Before the additional platforms were built at Tokyo Central, some peak time southbound trains used to terminate at Ueno, but this practice has now ceased.

Earlier, details were given of the Akita Shinkansen, which, like the line to Yamagata, requires the use of standard-gauge, high-speed trains built to the country's original loading gauge. The prototype E3 set for this route was completed in 1995 and was generally similar to the other 'Mini-Shinkansen' units (Series 400s), but had a higher maximum speed available on the main line, to enable the overall journey time to compete with the Akita–Tokyo air services. These trains are finished in their own distinctive livery, with silver-grey up to waist level, and white for the upper part of the bodies. A narrow cerise band separates the two colours, sweeping down to run round the end of the pointed nose. A large black panel stretches forward from the cab windows, with two marker lights in it to complement the four high-intensity ones at roof level, like those on the Series 400s. The colour schemes are designed to give a 'Gallant' external appearance, while 'Hospitality' and 'Spaciousness' are the themes for the interior.

Those of the E2 sets which have been fitted with couplers – known as E2[1] – work with the E3s between Tokyo and Morioka. They are built to full Shinkansen width, but their roof-line is even lower than that of the Series 400s, being no more than 3700 mm (12ft 1½ins) from the rail – only 50 mm (2 in.) less than the Series 300s – to minimise pressure-waves in the tunnels. The sets consist of eight cars, including a driving trailer at each end, all built from light alloy. Maximum axle-load is less than 13 tonnes. The Akita trains are capable of being coupled with either the E2[1]'s or the Series 200 sets, but will only be permitted to run at the full 275km/h with the former.

These full-sized units also have an internal 25 kV train-line running the length of the six central powered cars. A set has 630 ordinary seats in the usual 3+2 arrangement, while the single Green Car seats 51 in a 2+2 layout. Each block of seats is rotatable, and the triple ones have provision for the centre seat to slide backwards and forwards to enable the seats to be turned round. (A new seat-turning mechanism is also being developed to enable seat-capacities to be increased on the Series E1 sets). The Series E2s have a long, pointed nose, with the cab and its windows protruding from it in a way that is reminiscent of the Eurostars. There are, however, quite prominent 'shoulders' above and behind it, where the vehicle's cross-section becomes more rectangular, like that of the Series 300. Viewed from head-on, the fairings over the leading bogie have a shape that reminds one of those on the luxury Italian *Settobello* sets. The bogies generally are faired in to axle-level, in the interest of noise-suppression.

As with the Series E3s, the upper portion of the E2s is painted white, but a dark, metallic, 'Aster Blue' is used for the lower half. The two colours are separated by a crimson band, which is again carried down to run round the extreme front of the nose. Overall the designers have

Table 9.6
Tohoku, Joetsu & Nagano Shinkansen Train Services 2000
Numbers of Regularly-Scheduled Trains (Mondays–Fridays)

Train Type	Northbound	Southbound	Total
Tohoku Shinkansen			
Yamabiko	48	47	95
MAX Yamabiko	13	11	24
Nasuno	15	16	31
MAX Nasuno	0	1	1
Tsubasa	15	15	30
Komanchi	15	15	30
TOTALS	**106**	**105**	**211**
Joetsu Shinkansen			
Asahi	21	21	42
MAX Asahi	7	7	14
Tanigawa	16	16	32
MAX Tanigawa	3	4	7
TOTALS	**47**	**48**	**95**
Nagano Shinkansen			
Asama	28	28	56
TOTALS	**28**	**28**	**56**
GRAND TOTALS	**181**	**181**	**362**

Notes:
1. All *Tsubasa*, with the exception of two in each direction, run coupled with a *Yamabiko* between Tokyo and Fukushima.
2. All *Komanchi*, with the exception of one in each direction, run coupled with a *Yamabiko* between Tokyo and Morioka. One of them runs so coupled between Sendai and Morioka

Source: JR-E

adopted the Japanese *Yubi* concept, which denotes 'grace and beauty'. There are also a number of internal amenity improvements, including seats for the physically-handicapped, and separate 'Western-style' toilets for male and female use. Both feature larger wash-basins as well as 'odour-removing, heated toilet seats'. Luggage space is provided in the vestibules, as well as hand-grips, which passengers who are standing, ready to alight, will find helpful during the smart braking used when train is approaching a station stop.

Another new motive-power development for East Japan's high-speed lines appeared in late 1997. This was a new version of MAX, consisting of eight-car units which can be coupled together in pairs. So, for the first time there will be a 'multiple unit' system on the main Shinkansen lines, of the sort understood by this term in Europe. This provides flexibility to deal with loading variations during the day or along the line, as well as enabling them to split and combine at junctions. Since December 1999 two of the E4 *Yamabiko* services from Tokyo to Morioka split at Sendai, the rear 8-car set remaining at the last-named station for just over 3 hours, before being 'collected' on the return journey. Details of these E4 sets are given in Table 9.4.

In conclusion we need to put on record the average speeds that have been timetabled on the East Japan Shinkansen since Privatisation. The new timetable introduced in March 1988 saw times cut by quite significant amounts, not only on the Shinkansen, but to destinations which involved a change to 1067 mm-gauge trains. On the Tohoku Shinkansen there were cuts of 13 minutes between Ueno and Morioka, and 11 to and from Sendai. While

those changing at Morioka for an ordinary train to Akita only benefited from the 13 minutes saved on the high-speed section of the journey, there were cuts of over two hours between Tokyo and the cities of Sapporo and Hakodate in Hokkaido. The time to the former was still nearly 10 hours, however, so daytime rail journeys did not compete with air on a time basis. On the Joetsu Shinkansen there were cuts of 14 minutes to Niigata and 12 to Nagaoka.

Table 9.7 lists the fastest start-to-stop speeds scheduled on the JR-E Shinkansen between 1987 and 1991, taken from the *Railway Gazette International* biennial surveys. It was only in 1985 that the northern Shinkansen had appeared in the table, but they then did so almost to the complete exclusion of the Tokaido and Sanyo routes. The same applied in the next two surveys, but by 1993 the introduction of the Series 300 *Nozomi*, running long distances at 270 km/h, had, in turn, squeezed the JR-East trains out of this Japanese list, a situation which applied until 1999.

The other part of the *Railway Gazette International* survey lists a country's fastest overall railway journeys, inclusive of intermediate stops, and, as shown in Table 9.8, both northern Shinkansen routes have been represented in each survey since Privatisation, except that for 1997. The effects of the 1988 speed-up can be seen, but, from the average-speed columns, it may appear that there was a subsequent drop in performance. This is, however, explained by the opening of the extension from Ueno into Tokyo Central, a stretch of line where speed is severely limited. From the point of view of the overall journey times, the additional 3–4 minutes added to the times of the *Yamabiko* trains listed are significantly less than that spent previously getting to Ueno and changing trains. It is also interesting to note that, by 1993, *Tsubasa 101* had been listed in the world 'Top 30', in spite of the slow stretch over Itaya Pass.

Table 9.7
Fastest Tohoku and Joetsu Shinkansen Journeys, inclusive of intermediate stops 1987–1995

Year	Train	From*	To*	Distance km	miles	Time hr	min	No. of Stops	Speed km/h	mph
1987	8 *Yamabiko*	Ueno	Morioka	492.9	306.3	2	45	3	179.2	111.3
	6 *Asahi*	Ueno	Niigata	297.2	184.7	1	53	2	157.8	98.1
1989	4 *Yamabiko*	Morioka	Ueno	492.9	306.3	2	32	1	194.6	120.9
	2 *Asahi*	Ueno	Niigata	297.2	184.7	1	39	1	180.1	111.9
1991	4 *Yamabiko*	Ueno	Morioka	492.9	306.3	2	32	1	194.6	120.9
	2 *Asahi*	Ueno	Niigata	297.2	184.7	1	36	1	185.8	115.5
1993	4 *Yamabiko*	Morioka	Tokyo	496.5	308.5	2	36	1	191.0	118.7
	2 *Asahi*	Tokyo	Niigata	300.8	186.8	1	40	1	180.5	112.2
	Tsubasa 101	Tokyo	Yamagata	342.2	212.6	2	27	1	139.7	86.8
1995	*Max Yamabiko 4*	Morioka	Tokyo	496.5	308.5	2	35	1	191.0	118.7
	2 *Asahi*	Tokyo	Niigata	300.7	186.8	1	40	1	180.4	112.2
	Tsubasa 101	Tokyo	Yamagata	342.2	212.6	2	27	1	139.7	86.8
1997	*Yamabiko 14*	Morioka	Tokyo	496.5	308.5	2	20	1	212.8	132.2

* Some of the multiple journeys may be in the opposite direction.

Source: *Railway Gazette International*

Table 9.8
Tohoku and Joetsu Shinkansen Start-to-Stop Speeds over 200km/h 1987–1999

Year	Train	From*	To*	Distance km	miles	Time min	Speed km/h	mph
1987	6 *Yamabiko*	Morioka	Sendai	171.1	106.3	50	205.3	127.6
	6 *Yamabiko*	Fukushima	Omiya	223.8	139.1	66	203.5	126.4
	Yamabiko 22	Koriyama	Utsunomiya	104.9	65.2	31	203.0	126.1
	Yamabiko 10	Koriyama	Omiya	182.6	113.5	54	202.9	126.1
	6 *Yamabiko*	Sendai	Morioka	171.1	106.3	51	201.3	125.1
1989	6 *Yamabiko*	Morioka	Sendai	171.1	106.3	48	213.9	132.9
	3 *Yamabiko*	Omiya	Fukushima	223.8	139.1	64	209.8	130.4
	6 *Yamabiko*	Sendai	Morioka	171.1	106.3	49	209.5	130.2
	3 *Yamabiko*	Koriyama	Omiya	182.6	113.5	53	206.7	128.4
	3 *Yamabiko*	Fukushima	Omiya	223.8	139.1	65	206.6	128.4
	26 *Yamabiko*	Koriyama	Utsunomiya	104.9	65.2	31	203.0	126.1
1991	6 *Yamabiko*	Morioka	Sendai	171.1	106.3	48	213.9	132.9
	3 *Yamabiko*	Omiya	Fukushima	223.8	139.1	63	213.1	132.4
	6 *Yamabiko*	Sendai	Morioka	171.1	106.3	49	209.5	129.9
	Yamabiko 12	Koriyama	Omiya	223.8	139.1	65	206.6	128.4
	26 *Yamabiko*	Koriyama	Utsunomiya	104.9	65.2	31	203.0	126.1
1999	5 *Yamabiko*	Morioka	Sendai	171.1	106.3	43	238.7	148.3
	5 *Yamabiko*	Sendai	Omiya	294.1	182.7	75	235.3	146.2

* Some of the multiple journeys may be in the opposite direction.

Source: *Railway Gazette International*

CHAPTER 10
The Quest for Speed

During the 1990s, all three JR companies in Honshu developed even-faster Shinkansen trains, and each, in turn, established new national railway speed records. This culminated in JR-Central's '300X' train reaching 443.0 km/h (275.3 m.p.h.) in July 1996, which narrowed the gap with the SNCF's TGV-*Atlantique* set No. 325 to 72.3 km/h (44.9 m.p.h.). There was a very serious commercial purpose behind all this effort and expense, as the railways are anxious to maintain the various Shinkansen lines' share of the national transport market in Japan.

As we have seen, thirty-five years ago the commencement of high-speed services on the pioneering Tokaido Shinkansen ushered in a completely new era for railways throughout the world, and successive increases in service speed in Japan from 210 to 300 km/h (131 to 186 m.p.h.) have seen passenger numbers and revenue increase. That, in itself, provided a considerable incentive for the companies to develop even faster train services, but there is also steady public pressure to extend the advantages of shorter journey-times.

Nor must the competition from rival forms of transport be overlooked, particularly in the light of advances in air and road technology. The Sanyo and Chugoku Expressways west of Osaka were completed, and the Akashi-Kaikyo bridges were opened, including the world's longest suspension bridge, with a central span of 1.99 km (2176 yards), connecting Kobe with Awaji Island. The capacity and number of airports throughout the country is steadily increasing, but the 1994 opening of the massive Kansai International Airport on an artificial island in Osaka Bay benefits West Japan Railway by providing a new gateway for overseas travellers on their own doorstep.

In addition to these important factors, Japanese companies, and the country as a whole, spend a considerable portion of their income on long-term research, realising this is the only way of maintaining their technological position relative to the rest of the world. The flurry of activity that took place on the various Shinkansen routes in the 1990s has therefore to be seen in this overall context. The story of East Japan Railway's STAR 21 train has already been told in the previous chapter, and the highlights of other two Honshu railway companies' development work

will now be described, followed by descriptions of the new service trains and services on the Tokaido and Sanyo Shinkansen which resulted.

West Japan's WIN350

JR-West's fourth-generation experimental Shinkansen train was initially given the designation '500X', but this was soon altered to WIN350, which stood for **W**est Japan's **In**novation for operation at <u>**350**</u> km/h. The six-car unit was completed in March 1992, and had a strikingly different appearance from all earlier sets.

Compared with previous trains, the height of the light-alloy bodies was reduced by 700 mm (27½ in), and much larger pantograph shields of different shapes were provided to deflect the passing airflow away from the current-collecting equipment. This not only improved the efficiency of the operation, but reduced the production of the Karman vortices which generate noise. (These are the swirls of air produced alternately on the opposite sides of a thin rod or wire by a passing air stream, which, for example, make telephone wires hum in the wind. At Shinkansen speeds the 'hum' could become a major contribution to the noise generated by a passing train). The profiles of the set's driving cabs at the two ends were different, one being continuously curved both longitudinally and laterally, while the other had a raised central section like a variable-depth clerestory. The train was finished in a purple and light-blue livery, with some darker blue additions.

A number of important engineering changes were made, the most significant being the reduction of the maximum axle-load to 9.59 tonnes, while the whole train tared 230 tonnes. All axles were motored, using 300 kW (400 h.p.) three-phase motors, while the largest GTOs (**G**ate **T**urn-**O**ff thyristors) in the world were incorporated into the VVVF inverters which drove them. This enabled each of these installations to power six traction motors instead of the usual four. Lightweight transformers were also developed. The weight of the bogies themselves was reduced from 10 to 5.8 tonnes, and tests on the roller-rig showed they did not hunt at speeds of up to 500 km/h (310 m.p.h.), in spite of

Left: JR-West's first Series 500 Shinkansen on the occasion of its press roll-out in February 1996.
Mikio Miura

Above: Interior of Series 500 Green Car. Note curved body-sides.
Mikio Miura

Above: Cab of JR-West's Series 500 on test at 300 km/h.
JR-West

Above: Line-up of JR-West Shinkansen, February 1996. Left to right they are: Series 0, Series 100N, WIN350, Series 300 and Series 500.
Mikio Miura

Below: JR-West's Series 500 prototype at Hiroshima in May 1996.
Mikio Miura

Table 10.1 Comparison of Contact Wires			
	All-copper	Copper/steel	Aluminum/steel
Tension (kN)	15.0	19.6	14.7
Cross-section (mm²)	170	110	200
Line density (kg/m)	1.511	0.942	0.758
Diffusion rate (km/h)	355	520	496

Source: JR-C, JEEE Vol 116, No.4 (1996)

their 2500 mm (8ft 8in) wheelbase. Three types of primary suspension were provided on different bogies to compare their performance.

Provision was made for full-length sound-proofing skirts to be tested to determine how effectively they would reduce lateral noise emission from the underside of the train, particularly the bogies. The cars were later provided with tilting equipment to reduce the effect of excess centrifugal forces on curves, and an active suspension was fitted to stop excessive lateral movements of the body relative to the bogies during high-speed curving.

Before full-speed trials were started with WIN350, various infrastructure improvements were also carried out along the test section between Ogori and Shin-Shimonoseki at the western end of Honshu. Cant was increased on curves, and an elastomer mat inserted between the ballast and the slab deck of viaducts to reduce ground vibration. The rail heads were carefully ground smooth to minimise noise-production as the wheels passed over them at high speeds. Composite contact wires were used on the overhead power supply system to improve collection efficiency and the wave velocity, which is a measure of how quickly the wire reacts to the approach of a pantograph. Table 10.1 compares the different types of wire tried on JR-West as well as on other lines where speeds in excess of 300 km/h (186 m.p.h.) have been run experimentally.

The original all-copper wire was comparable in size to the one used on the old Woodhead and Shenfield 1500 V d.c. electrifications in the UK. The Japanese copper/steel replacement is almost exactly the same size as our present 25 kV contact wires, so is appreciably lighter than their standard type. Because of the higher resistance of the steel core, it has a lower electrical conductivity, but the over-line wiring, as a whole, is designed to carry the same amount of current. By virtue of its higher strength, the steel enables it to be tensioned with a third as much force again, which improves the dynamic performance as the pantographs pass. The aluminum/steel version is lighter still, and has a wave velocity that is more than 60% higher than the former plain copper wire. The aluminium/steel version is only half the weight of the all-copper standard, but is similarly tensioned.

Changes were also made in the cab signalling system to permit WIN350 to run at higher speeds than the normal 270 km/h (168 m.p.h.) permitted for the Series 300 Nozomi. Trials with WIN350 began in June 1992, and between 21 July and 8 August that year it successively reached speeds of 303.0, 345.8 and 350.4 km/h (188.3, 214.9 and 217.7 m.p.h.). These were attained at the foot of the slightly falling gradient at km.Post 964.3, west of Ogori in Yamaguchi prefecture. As shown in Table 10.2, the second of these marginally exceeded the previous national record, which had been set up by the prototype Series 400 'Mini-Shinkansen' in September 1991. The final run fractionally exceeded the world record that had been achieved by DB's InterCityExperimental near Bergsinn in 1986.

As part of their development work on current collection, JR-West developed a completely new system for use on the WIN350. Instead of the numerous small-diameter rods used in the construction of a conventional pantograph, the new device consisted of two aerofoils arranged in the shape of a letter 'T'. The stem rode up and down in a sleeve installed in the roof of the coach, to keep the top surface of the cross-bar in touch with the contact wire. There were the usual contact strips on this, and the downward-pointing 'horns' at its ends were also aerofoil in cross-section.

In the latest nomenclature, this device is referred to as a 'Current Collector', which the writer supports wholeheartedly, as it is incorrect to call it a 'pantograph'. The latter name is derived from 'an instrument for copying a plan or drawing', to quote the Concise Oxford Dictionary. The similarity of that outdated drawing-office item to a conventional pantograph on an electric train is obvious, and the latter was undoubtedly named to distinguish it from the earlier bow-collectors and trolley poles. Even the so-called 'single-arm pantographs' actually have a less-obvious second parallel set of rods, so still retain the essentials of the original draftsman's aid. Regardless of these semantics, the aerofoil current collector is a very efficient device, and it subsequently appeared on the commercial Series 500 sets.

After the completion of its trials, the experimental WIN350 set was withdrawn, and a special farewell ceremony was held on 30 May 1996 at Hakata depot. The two end cars have been preserved. One of them joined the collection at the excellent Transport Science Museum at Osaka, while the other is on exhibition at Maibara, the location of the Railway Technical Resarch Institute's new low-noise wind tunnel.

The Series 500 Shinkansen

Following JR-West's work with its WIN350, plans were announced in September 1994 for the introduction of a new commercial train, the Series 500, and service running began in the financial year 1997/8. These are full-length 16-car sets, capable of taking advantage of the higher speeds possible on the Sanyo Shinkansen, where they reach maxima of 300 km/h (186 m.p.h.).

The design represented a dramatic change from all previous Japanese high-speed trains for their main lines, as it has an almost circular cross-section, in contrast to the earlier ones, which had been basically rectangular with rounded corners. To enclose a given area, a circle has the lowest periphery, and the lightest structure to provide a given passenger space on a train is thus a cylinder. This shape is also very efficient from the strength point of view, particularly when there is a differential pressure across it, as was demonstrated by the use of circular cross-sectioned boilers for steam locomotives.

A cylindrical shape can nowadays be fabricated from the lightweight brazed-honeycomb sandwich materials available, and the Series 500 is constructed in this way. Great care was taken to produce the smoothest possible exterior, which looks much more like an elongated aircraft fuselage than a train. The maximum exterior width is 3380 mm (11.1 ft), which is the same as all previous commercial trains on the Tokaido and Sanyo Shinkansen routes. The maximum height of the roof (3690 mm, 12.1 ft) is actually marginally greater than that of the Series 300s. By fixing the floor height so that the maximum interior width coincides with the hip-level of seated passengers, full use is made of the space, and the 'tumblehome' at shoulder level is no different from that on the UK MkIV coaches. The usual 2+3 seating is provided in the ordinary coaches, with a 2+2 arrangement in the Green Cars. The new train can seat 1124 ordinary passengers and 200 Green Car ones, giving a total of 1324, the same as a Series 300. Particular care is being given to the overall ambience of the interior. Service counters are available in two cars, which sell lunch-boxes, souvenirs, special local foods and other items.

Externally the Series 500 has recaptured and amplified the 'Bullet Train' image, with its cylindrical shape and extended nose. The end coaches are a full two metres (6½ ft) longer than the other cars, which are the usual 25 metres over couplings. This shape is not just a design feature but is to minimise noise problems in the numerous tunnels along the Sanyo Shinkansen, as described later. There is a bubble-shaped canopy for the driving cab, which is not all that dissimilar to the ones on the Eurostars, although the 'JR-West' blue panel extending forwards from it is much more tasteful than the yellow patch on the front of our cross-Channel trains. There are similarly-coloured panels enclosing the windows, and on the roof, with the remainder of the exterior being in a blue-white shade. The high-powered headlights are set behind curved covers at the bottom corners of the windscreen.

All the axles on the train are powered, with the usual VVVF-powered ac traction motors, rated at 285 kW (380 h.p.) each. The maximum power available is thus 18.24 MW, which equates to no less than 24 450 h.p. This gives the train a residual acceleration of 0.26 km/h/sec (0.24 ft/sec²) at the design speed of 320 km/h (199 m.p.h.), and a balancing speed of 365 km/h (227 m.p.h.) on level track. A Series 500 has a pair of wing-shaped current collectors, with low fairings over the insulators on which they are mounted. The horns on their lateral ends have been reduced to oval rods, with longitudinal holes bored through them to break up the vortices. The high-voltage roof-line connections are now made between coaches with insulated cables, and their ends are faired into the roofs of the coaches, which makes the assembly a lot more streamlined than previously.

In 1996 JR-West ordered nine of the Series 500 sets for commercial service, and the first three entered service in March 1997. Their introduction marked the first 300 km/h passenger operation in Japan, making that country 'first-equal' with the SNCF and Spanish high-speed trains. It is possible to run at this speed for a significant length of the Sanyo route, in spite of the environmental constraints which do not apply to the European lines. (Central France is sometimes referred to by geographers as the 'Wyoming of Europe', and the AVE does not pass through much habitation between Madrid and Seville in Spain). As a result, by 1999 the overall timing for one train over the 553.7 km (344 miles) between Shin-Osaka and Hakata had come down to 2hr 17min, inclusive of three intermediate stops - a cut of 15min on the 1996 timing, corresponding to a speed of 242.5 km/h (150.7 m.p.h.). The fastest twelve start-to-stop runs with the Series 500s in 1999 were over the 192.0 km (119.3 miles) between Hiroshima and Kokura, where the average was no less than 261.8 km/h (162.7 m.p.h.). The fastest such speeds attained by seven TGVs between St. Pierre des Corps and Massy TGV at that time was 253.3 km/h (157.4 m.p.h.).

In March 1997 the author rode in one of the Series 500s from Okayama to Shin-Osaka, which, in spite of speed restrictions at the eastern end, covered the 100.0 miles in 44min 40sec, at an average of 261.1 km/h (134.3 m.p.h.). Our timing as an extra train was not quite as fast as those

for the subsequent scheduled services, two of which are booked to cover the distance in 40 min, one in each direction. During the short time each of the overseas visitors was able to get into the cab, the speedometer was clearly seen to be registering 300 km/h.

Central Japan's '300X' Project

Although the last of the 1990s' experimental Shinkansen trains is designated '300X', that item of rolling-stock is only one part of Central Japan Railway's '300X Shinkansen Project'. Its mission statement 'Aiming for the Best and Most Advanced High-Speed Railway System Possible', and, as we will see later, the results of this work have already resulted in the development, jointly with JR-West, of a new Shinkansen train – the Series 700.

The '300X Project' is divided into two parts:

- Establishing the techniques to construct a high-speed railway system.
- Obtaining data of various sorts about high-speed rail travel.

The main lines of activity are:

- Development of a system to run stably at high speed.
- Development of a braking system to work stably at high speed.
- Exploring aerodynamic problems.
- Preserving the environment.
- Improving the ride comfort.
- Maintaining a high-speed and high-density transport capacity.

Each of these involve three successive stages of investigation. In the first, simulation work is carried out using powerful computers and models developed from existing data. Then the critical aspects are tested in 'laboratory' conditions, using, for example, a wind tunnel to determine aerodynamic characteristics. Finally there are full-size running tests, which is where the '300X' train came into the picture.

From the public's point of view, the most obvious part of this programme is the six-car experimental '300X' train, which was delivered in January 1995. It is finished in the familiar white and blue livery of the Series 300, but the cars on the '300X' are 7¾ in narrower and 11 in lower than those of the previous design. The inner cars are the usual 25 m over couplings, but the two lead vehicles are much longer than those on the Series 300 – 27.2 m compared with 26.1 (89¼ and 85½ ft respectively). Like the other experimental trains described earlier, the design included a number of alternative options so these could be evaluated, the most obvious again being the shape of the ends. One of these is a rounded wedge, and the other a cusp, which makes it look somewhat like the beak of a duck. The smaller cross-section of the cars, plus the under-nose and side fairings, reduced the aerodynamic drag by 22%, and fitting shrouds over the bogies dropped it by another 8%. It was reckoned that the streamlining applied by Gresley to his 'A4s' made only a marginal reduction in the train's overall drag, but things are very different at 300 km/h!

Back in JNR days, most of the rolling-stock was designed jointly by the railway and the firms which constructed its car-bodies and equipment. JNR used to purchase rolling stock to an agreed design, which enabled it to obtain similar vehicles from different manufacturers. This arrangement has changed since Privatisation, and each of the railways

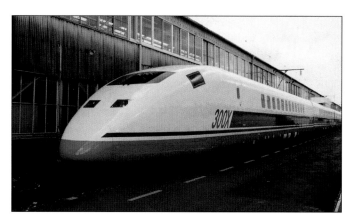

Above left: A motor bogie of the '300X' (right) compared with one for the Series 300. The longer wheelbase is obvious, as it the raised airbag suspension. The relative size of the traction motors is also interesting, as those on the '300X' have a peak output of 500 kW (670 h.p.) compared with 300 kW (400 h.p.) for the series 300 design. *JR-Central*

Above right: The 'Round-Wedge' end of JR-Central's '300X' test train, which holds the Japanese rail speed record of 443 km/h (275.3 mph). *JR-Central*

Right: The 'Cusp' end of JR-Central's '300X' test train at the time of its press preview. *JR-Central*

Above: '300X' undergoing 'slow-speed' trials (up to 270 km/h) on the Tokaido Shinkansen during daylight. Round-wedge end leading. *JR-Central*

Below left and right: The unusual mounting for the pantographs on '300X', viewed from above level (left) and ground level (right). *JR-Central/Kazumiki Miura*

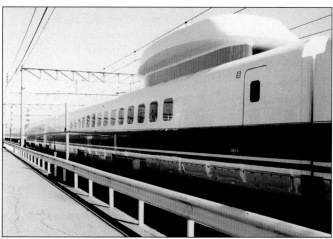

Facing page top: JR-West's Series 500 prototype near Hakata in May 1996. *Mikio Miura*

Facing page bottom: JR-West's WIN 350 emerges from the Kanmon Tunnel near Shimonoseki after travelling under the strait separating Kyushu from Honshu. *Mikio Miura*

now issues a 'Performance Specification', as was done by BR during its final years. The manufacturers, together with the railway staff, are then involved in working out the detailed proposals, the two parties finally agreeing the design. When it goes into service, responsibility is shared between the operating railway and the manufacturers, depending on the nature of any defect.

Four very different methods of construction were adopted for the six cars in the '300X' train, and each type came from a different manufacturer. The use of light-weight body-shells brought the axleloads for the '300X' down to the range 8.0–9.0 tonnes, which is a useful reduction on the 10.1 achieved with the Series 300s.

The bogie wheelbase on the '300X' was increased from the usual 2500 mm to 3000, to improve stability. At the 'laboratory-testing' stage they were put through their paces on the roller-rig at speeds of up to 500 km/h (310 m.p.h.). As with Series 500, the secondary suspension is provided by airbags, but, to improve stability, these are mounted 1.7 m above the rails instead of the previous 1.0 (5.6 ft rather than 3.3), which raises their attachments above the bodies' centres of gravity. On some of the cars, the pillars to which they are fixed enclose hydraulic rams which provide a tilting action on curves. Another similar system, operating in the horizontal plane, forms an active suspension, and so prevents any lateral buffeting during curving.

All axles are driven by the usual VVVF-powered a.c. traction motors, but of higher power (500 kW, 670 h.p.), so the total available from all six motored cars of the '300X' are the same as that on a 16-car Series 300, with its 10 motor coaches. However, in the case of '300X' these are 15-minute ratings rather than continuous ones, which is quite adequate for test purposes. The train thus has a maximum power:weight ratio of 56kW/tonne (75 h.p./ton), which should be compared with the figure of 13.8 kW/tonne for a one of the shortened UK East Coast formations (Class 91 + 5 + DVT), as used for the various record-breaking runs. The faster acceleration from the '300X' enables the train to reach speeds of over 350 km/h on the short length of the track used for tests. (Before any tests could take place, considerable changes had to be made to the infrastructure. The ordinary contact wire had to be replaced with the aluminum/steel or copper/steel compound type, and its tension increased, as described earlier in this chapter).

When a train is travelling at 300 km/h, it covers 91 yards every second. If the passenger is to have a smooth ride, there must be no significant wave-irregularities in the rail surface over such a distance. These are difficult to measure, as well as requiring a lot of attention by the permanent-way staff to eliminate. On ordinary ballasted track the sleepers sink uniformly as the train passes over them, so maintaining a constant 'top', as set up by the tamper. There is, however, a particular problem with underbridges and viaducts, because these flex vertically to varying extents across the span. In the UK this problem worried BR when it was upgrading its main lines in the 1970s for 100 m.p.h. running. Fortuitously the original design of many of its small underbridges enabled them to be rebuilt to take ballasted track, rather than leaving the rails fixed to the old wooden or steel way-beams. On the Tokaido Shinkansen it is not possible to convert the viaducts to take ballasted track, so there are differences in 'elasticity' between the centre of a span and its points of support over the piers. As in the UK, the standard method of fixing rails to the sleepers is to use 'Pandrol' clips. One

of the other new developments tested as part of the '300X' programme are composition sleepers supported by anti-vibration pads on steel-truss bridges. These prevent axle-load fluctuations at high speeds, and so give excellent running stability.

Alterations to the Automatic Train Control system were made to permit the '300X' to run at over 270 km/h. This was achieved by installing a transponder in the track at each end of the super-high-speed section. As the train passes over the first one, it picks up a signal which resets its ATC to the new speed ranges, enabling the driver to accelerate. At the exit end, a second transponder cancels the special signal, and the train has to slow to normal speeds.

As we saw earlier, the standard ATC system uses a series of decelerations, separated by periods of coasting. As the time approaches for this system to be upgraded, JR-Central is using microelectronics and other state-of-the-art technologies to develop new equipment with improved reliability. It will replace the present multi-step deceleration with a smoother, single-stage, version, with data on the positions of the train and the one in front being continuously monitored. This will be used to bring the second train smoothly to a halt from whatever speed it is doing. Comprehensive trials are continuing with the '300X' to verify the functioning of the system and establish a specification for the equipment.

As has been said several times previously in this book, the major problem to be overcome every time Shinkansen speeds rise is to ensure that the trains do not breach the strict environmental requirements for noise and vibration. There are thus considerable advantages in making trains smaller and lighter, as well as reducing the generation of noise from various parts of them. Reference has already been made to the pantographs and bogies, but there is also a need to find out more about the way in which the large, relatively slow, flows of air that surround a train travelling at high speed can spin-off a series of small vortices which generate noise.

Another long-standing problem is the production of 'sonic booms', which have been apparent since the early days at the exit end of the tunnels used on the Sanyo Shinkansen, which are of smaller diameter the those on the earlier Tokaido Line. As a high-speed train enters a tunnel, any sudden irregularities in its shape displace the air ahead and alongside it, and these movements can react with the geometry of the 'hole' to produce a pressure wave. This is then transmitted along the tunnel at a rate which outstrips even the fastest Shinkansen. As this occurs, the pressure 'front' becomes more concentrated, so that, when it reaches the other end, it can emerge as a 'sonic boom', or cause windows to rattle, neither being popular with those living nearby.

The German high-speed ICEs on their *Neubaustrecke* cause similar problems, which are worse with tunnels about 1500 metres long. Shorter ones do not provide time for the wave to concentrate, while in longer ones it is attenuated by friction with the interior surfaces. Various factors affect the problem, ballasted track damping the waves more than the slab version, as used on the Sanyo line, where entry 'hoods' have had to be constructed in some places. These were matters looked at under the '300X' project, some of the aerodynamic work being too difficult to carry out in a wind-tunnel. Lineside measurements were made during test runs to determine the detail of what was happening, so the computer models could be improved.

The same process was adopted in the investigations taking place to determine the interactions between wheel and rail. JR-Central leased a computer package VAMPIRE (**Ve**hicle **D**ynamic **M**odelling **P**ackage **i**n a **R**ailway **E**nvironment) from AEA Technology (formerly part of British Rail Research), and measurements made during the test runs were fed into this simulation to give a better understanding of what was happening at the vital points where the vehicle is being supported and guided.

Trial running with the '300X' train began in January 1995, and, with speeds no higher than 270 km/h, this work was carried out on an 'ordinary' stretch of Shinkansen track, between Shizuoka and Hamamatsu. The only part of the Tokaido Shinkansen suitable for higher speeds than this is between Kyoto and Maibara, where there is a 25 km (15½ mile) stretch over which it is possible to run at more than 350 km/h (217 m.p.h.). It does not pass through any tunnels, but it does include one short viaduct. As more than 100 trains a day use the line in each direction every day of the year, testing can only take place when normal traffic has ceased. Normally the Shinkansen tracks are closed to everything except slow-speed engineering trains for the six hours from midnight, but JR-C was able to make a 'slot' for one test run on any given night. This is fitted in immediately after the last commercial services of the day, taking into account maintenance work and the residential environment.

The test programme is scheduled to continue until the end of 2002, during which some 600 running tests will have been carried out, usually at the rate of two per week. On the day of each test, the staff involved, numbering up to 40, attend a briefing session at Hamamatsu in the evening, before boarding the train for the 237 km (147 mile) run to Shin-Osaka. This takes place at commercial speeds between ordinary services, and enables the crew to check and calibrate their equipment. The train then returns over the 39 km (24 miles) to Kyoto for final checks, allowing the last passenger services to pass.

When the train starts its test run, speed is held at a maximum of 270 km/h until the transponder resets the ATC limits, whereupon the driver accelerates up to the limit fixed for that particular test. Twenty-odd kilometres further on, the second transponder signals the approaching end of the super-high-speed section, and the train starts to brake, finally coming to a stop in the platform loop at Maibara. Various checks are then made of the equipment, and the test crew transfers to their overnight hotel after the final debriefing, making such a test very demanding.

It was in May 1995 that the trials were switched to this second site, and speeds were increased to a nominal ceiling of 350 km/h (217 m.p.h.). On 21 September a speed of 354.1 km/h (220 m.p.h.) was reached, which confirmed that the vehicle performance and the ground facilities were stable at the initial target speed of 350 km/h. A further series of trials started in April 1996 to push the maximum still higher, and on 11 July '300X' topped the speed of 425.0 km/h reached by STAR 21 in late 1993, so JR-Central now held the Japanese rail speed record. Then on 26 July the '300X' lifted this by a further 10 m.p.h., reaching no less than 443.0 km/h (275.3 m.p.h.).

In five and a half years the Japanese railways thus raised their national rail speed record by no less than 117.3 km/h (72.9 m.p.h.). Details of all the significant speed attainments by Shinkansen trains are given in Table 10.2. The '300X' project thus added a significant final contribution to the remarkable successes the other experimental

Shinkansen trains had achieved during the four-year period from 1992. In addition to the resulting development of the Series 700 units, as we will see later in this chapter, the experimental work by this train will continue for a further two years.

At the end of the 1997 International High-Speed Railway Conference hosted by JR-Central and JR-West, delegates were treated to a midnight trip on the '300X' unit over the test section of the Tokaido Line, where it had achieved its 443.0 km/h (275.3 m.p.h.) the previous year. Our special high-speed run, like all the other test ones with '300X', took place after all service trains had cleared the area, and we were given a count-down over the public address system before we departed at exactly 23.59. The rear of the cabs on the '300X' are wide open to the coach, and no less than seven of the visitors were lucky in the draw for the enviable seats behind the driver.

Those of us not at the front-end had a closed-circuit video screen to watch, giving a view of the track ahead, with a large digital speedometer on the end bulkhead. We rapidly reached 75 m.p.h. and cruised at about this speed for some five minutes before a second count-down began. Then the 16 085 h.p. available power to all the axles was unleashed, and speed rose quickly. From 140 to 350 km/h my timings from the speedometer showed the speed increasing as follows:

Speed		Time
(km/h)	(mph)	(sec)
140	87	0
160	99	22
180	112	46
200	124	65
220	137	83
240	149	97
260	162	116
280	174	132
300	186	150
320	199	170
340	211	190
350	217	200

Up to about 200 km/h we were taking over 11 sec. to accelerate by each successive 10 km/h, but this was followed by a more rapid gain, with only about 8 sec. being needed for a similar increase. As speed got higher still the acceleration fell off somewhat, but each increase of 10 km/h was still only occupying about 10 sec. All told our speed went up by 210 km/h (130 m.p.h.) in a total of 200 sec.

When we got to this speed I transferred my attention to the video, and discovered I could pick up the reflective kilometre markers on the lineside masts as they shot past the cab, which enabled me to do some conventional timing – at 218 m.p.h. in the middle of the night! The maximum of 351 km/h which I recorded in this way agreed well with the official maximum of 351.6 (218.5 m.p.h.). To provide a comparison with UK performance, such a speed was only 1½ m.p.h. less than the *combined* speeds of a passing pair of our West Coast expresses!

The only other sensation at this speed was a rumble under the floor, and it would have been understandable if the passengers had thought the whole trip was an example of large-scale Virtual Reality! However, when we alighted after the 25½ min journey, we were clearly in a very different station. And, with the Shinkansen system then shut down for its nightly six-hour maintenance period, it took us the best part of two hours to get back to our start

Above: The plaque on the side of JR-Central's '300X' commemorating its record speed achieved on 26 July 1996.   *Mikio Miura*

Right: Well after midnight the author pauses for a souvenir photograph alongside JR-Central's '300X' experimental train in Maibara station which had just reached 351.6 km/h (218.5 m.p.h.) on a demonstration run in March 1997.

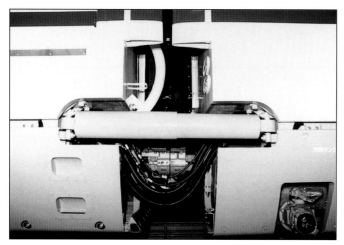

Above: Anti-yaw damper between adjacent coaches of JR-Central Series 700 train.

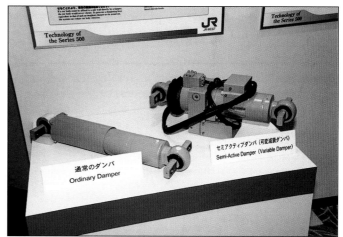

Above: A semi-active damper for a Series 500 Shinkansen compared with an ordinary damper.   *Yoshihiko Sato*

Below: A JR-West series 700 Hikari Rail Star passes a Series 0 in Asa station in March 2000.   *Mikio Miura*

Above: Rape starts to blossom in the fields as a JR-Central Series 700 speeds past Mount Fuji. *Mikio Miura*

Right: A mid-winter view of Mount Fuji from a passing Shinkansen. *Mikio Miura*

Two notable rolling-stock events on the Tokaido Shinkansen

Below left: The first passenger service by a Series 700 *Nozomi* gets ready to leave Tokyo Central station on 13 March 1999. *Mikio Miura*

Below right: With a special 'head mark' the last JR-Central Kodama working with a Series O leaves Tokyo Central in the dusk on 12 September 1999. *Kazumiki Miura*

ing point by road! It is clear that there were many advanced features that could be incorporated into the forthcoming Series 700 Shinkansen, which combined the technology of the '300X' with that of the Series 500.

Series 700 Shinkansen

The July 1996 agreement between JR-West and JR-Central had the object of developing a new series of Shinkansen trains for their through services on the Tokaido and Sanyo routes. JR-Central supplied the technology developed in the Series 300 and 300X programmes, while JR-West contributed the know-how that had introduced speeds of 300 km/h (186 m.p.h.) with the Series 500s. In this way it was planned to produce a single new series of trains with increased passenger comfort and reduced interior noise, while benefiting from the advantages of train-operation efficiency and cost reduction. (One of the full-length new trains only costs the same as a Series 300, which is considerably less than that of a Series 500).

Further details of the new train, provisionally referred to as 'N300' were announced in September 1996, but it later became the Series 700, of which 17 sets were ordered by JR-Central. Each consists of the usual 16 coaches, seating 1323 passengers, to facilitate inter-operability, and weighs less than a Series 300 (711 tonnes), of which a further 22 sets were ordered by JR-Central for delivery by 2000. Unlike the Series 500, on which all axles are motored, the Series 700s include four trailers, (two less than the Series 300s). The total installed power of each of these units is, however, 13.20MW (17 960 h.p.), which is eight% up on the Series 300, giving it a higher performance, which is utilised on the through Tokyo–Hakata *Nozomi* services, now worked by these trains.

The car bodies are constructed from hollow-extrusion aluminium-alloy sections, which provides better sound insulation. A new type of semi-conductor equipment – the Insulated Gate Bipolar Transistor (IGBT) – transmits the power to the traction motors. These devices had for some time been used in less powerful equipment for tramcars, etc, but have now been developed so they can replace the Gate Turn-Off thyristors (GTOs) which have been used in recent years for high-power traction motors. IGBTs are lighter, more reliable, and the installations are effectively quieter in operation because their faster operating frequency (up to 2000 Hz compared with 400–500 Hz for GTOs) moves the 'hum' produced from the electrical equipment to a higher pitch than most human ears can detect.

The profile of the end vehicles came as somewhat of a surprise, as they have nothing of the simple geometry that had previously been used for the earlier Shinkansen units. Not only are the end cars of the Series 700 longer than those on the Series 500, but they have an 'Aerostream' design, in which the cross-section area of the body increases linearly from the front at an optimised rate. To balance the 'discontinuities' formed by the cab windscreen, there are various 'bulges' further forward and behind it, an arrangement which markedly reduces the tendency for a train to produce 'shock-waves' as it enters a tunnel at speed. This shape provides another important benefit at the rear of the train, where it reduces the production of oscillating Karman vortices, which can be large enough to degrade the ride quality. These trains are also fitted with other specialised equipment to improve the ride. Longitudinal and lateral dampers are fitted between adjacent cars, and a semi-active lateral damping system is fitted to the bogies

of the end vehicles, the Green Cars and those carrying the pantographs. Their damping effect is varied virtually instantaneously by a microprocessor.

Line-side noise is also improved by the new nose, as well as the smoother surfaces of the car-bodies, the smoothed underfloor areas, and the use of high-performance single-arm pantographs. These have streamlined 'ramps' mounted on the roof in front of and behind them, with vertical sound baffles on each side, like miniature versions of the smoke-deflectors used on some steam locomotives. Ground vibration is reduced by the lightweight construction and equalisation of axle-loads.

From the passengers' point of view, various important improvements have been made to the interior of the coaches. By repositioning some of the air ducts, the ceiling height has been raised by 65 mm. (2½ in.), and its large curves give a sense of depth. The width of the centre aisle has been increased by ¾ of an inch (30 mm.) in all cars. (As usual, the standard class coaches have a 2+3 seating arrangement, with 2+2 in the Green Cars). For the first time on Shinkansen trains a two-stage air conditioning system has been used. Air from the exterior is cooled in the first stage, and then mixed with that being recirculated before the combined flow finally cooled to the desired temperature. The ducts are mounted below the generously-sized luggage racks, which cuts down the heat loss. Circulation is by small, high-speed fans, which, with sound-insulation, are much quieter than the earlier arrangements.

Steps have also been taken to minimise maintenance effort. Underfloor equipment-covers provide access from the *sides* of the train, and 'boltless' covers are used for the equipment, to reduce the time taken if they have to be

Date	Type/ Series	Location	Speed km/h	mph
31 Oct 1962	B	Kamonomiya test track	200.0	125.0
30 Mar 1963	B	Kamonomiya test track	256.0	159.0
24 Feb 1972	951	Sanyo Line	286.0	177.7
28 Nov 1979	961	Oyama test track	292.0	181.0
30 Nov 1979	961	Oyama test track	304.0	189.0
7 Dec 1979	961	Oyama test track	319.0	198.2
22 Sep 1983	925	Tohokuo Line	240.0	149.0
29 Oct 1984	925	Tohoku Line	261.0	162.0
21 Oct 1985	925	Tohoku Line	272.0	169.0
20 Aug 1985	100	Tokaido line	230.0	143.0
2 Sep 1985	100	Sanyo Line	260.0	162.0
20 Nov 1986	200	Tokoku Line	271.0	168.0
2 Dec 1988	200	Tohoku Line	276.0	171.0
8 Sep 1989	200/2000	Joetsu Line	275.0	170.9
28 Feb 1991	300	Tokaido Line	325.7	202.4
26 Mar 1991	400	Joetsu Line	336.0	208.8
19 Sep 1991	400	Joetsu Line	345.0	214.4
21 Jul 1992	WIN350	Sanyo Line	303.0	188.3
6 Aug 1992	WIN350	Sanyo Line	345.8	214.9
8 Aug 1992	WIN350	Sanyo Line	350.4	217.7
30 Oct 1992	STAR 21	Joetsu Line	353.0	219.3
1 Nov 1992	STAR 21	Joetsu Line	358.0	222.5
10 Sep 1993	STAR 21	Joetsu Line	363.6	225.9
15 Sep 1993	STAR 21	Joetsu Line	372.0	231.1
13 Dec 1993	STAR 21	Joetsu Line	420.0	261.0
21 Dec 1993	STAR 21	Joetsu Line	425.0	264.1
21 Sep 1995	300X	Tokaido Line	354.1	220.0
11 Jul 1996	300X	Tokaido Line	426.6	265.1
26 Jul 1996	300X	Tokaido Line	443.0	275.3

Sources: JNR, Murray Hughes *Rail 300* (and translations), JR-C, JR-E.

Left: A JR-Central Series 700 *Nozomi* at speed passing Odawara.　*Mikio Miura*

Japan's water features provide splendid settings for JR-Central's Shinkansen

Right: In the Spring a Series 300 speeds past a woman planting rice in a paddy field

Below: An autumn scene as a Series 700 *Nozomi* crosses a viaduct near Okayama on the Sanyo Shinkansen.
Mikio Miura (2)

94

TOKYO — NAGOYA — KYOTO — HIROSHIMA — HAKATA (TOKAIDO & SANYO SHINKANSEN)

Stations	N 25	N 63	K 479	H 135	661	K 385	H 253	H 255	H 257	663	K 521	H 169	K 481	H 259	H 171	K 435	H 387	N 65	K 593	H 27	595	K 665	N 29	H 265	K 483	H 263	H 171	K 435	H 387	N 173	K 485	N 31	H 267	H 269	K 525	N 69
東京 Tokyo Lv.	1752	1800	1810	1807		1814	1821	1828			1851	1845	1842	1838		1907	1900			1852			1956	1945	1942	1938	2110	2021	2035	2014			2038	2049	2056	2118
新横浜 Shin-Yokohama	1809		1827	1823		1830					1909		1855				1909							2001	1955		2122						2055		2113	2134
小田原 Odawara			1851								1913		1901			1948								2027				2102							2133	
熱海 Atami			1901								1923		1957			1959								2048						2057					2143	
三島 Mishima			1912								1937	1944		1951		2012								2104				2124							2151	
新富士 Shin-Fuji			1925								1948					2025								2118	2051											
静岡 Shizuoka			1939								2004			2027		2039								2140	2117											
掛川 Kakegawa			1959								2024					2101								2152												
浜松 Hamamatsu			2015								2038			2052	2117	2113								2206				2110	2122			2213	2234	2242		2257
豊橋 Toyohashi			2034								2054					2134								2208				2122						2247		
三河安城 Mikawa-Anjo			2053								2111					2155								2228												
名古屋 Nagoya	1934	1938	2105	2003		2054	2009	2013	2023		2124	2052		2131	2152	2215	2206			2131			2212	2245	2231	2213	2139	2204	2310	2251			2323	2339		2334
岐阜羽島 Gifu-Hashima						2110	2025					2149				2228	2209							2256	2247		2202	2224		2307			2339			2348
米原 Maibara	2012	2015		2047			2102	2102	2107		2147	2202				2245	2233			2228		2238			2326		2139	2239		2321			2343			
京都 Kyoto	2028	2030		2058			2118	2118	2123		2158	2212				2257			2133			2253														
新大阪 Shin-Osaka	2044	2106		2111			2123	2123	2132	2147	2211	2228		2257		2310	2257	2315	2246	2211	2320	2317	2211			2323						2353				
新神戸 Shin-Kobe										2158				2323			2330	2351	2303		2351	2347														
西明石 Nishi-Akashi	2109			2139	2144		2139		2133			2241									2353															
姫路 Himeji				2146	2158				2147	2211		2257			2246						2359															
相生 Aioi	2144			2214	2218		2241		2158						2303																					
岡山 Okayama				2229	2230				2241	2246		2328			2328																					
新倉敷 Shin-Kurashiki				2303	2245										2304																					
新尾道 Shin-Onomichi					2255																															
三原 Mihara					2300																															
東広島 Higashi-Hiroshima					2321																															
広島 Hiroshima				2304	2333										2323	2341																				
新岩国 Shin-Iwakuni																																				
徳山 Tokuyama				2323											2341																					
小郡 Ogori																																				
厚狭 Asa																																				
新下関 Shin-Shimonoseki	2228																																			
小倉 Kokura	2228			2323																																
博多(福岡) Hakata(Fukuoka) Ar.	2245			2341																																

HAKATA — HIROSHIMA — KYOTO — NAGOYA — TOKYO (TOKAIDO & SANYO SHINKANSEN)

Stations	K 520	K 522	K 524	K 526	K 528	K 442	K 444	K 446	K 448	K 200	K 202	H 40	K 450	K 530	H 204	H 206	K 140	H 2	H 452	K 208	K 142	K 454	K 210	H 212	H 110	H 600	H 602	K 456	K 214	K 402	H 216	H 218	H 220	H 604	K 350	H 146	H 144	H 352	N 6	K 460
博多(福岡) Hakata(Fukuoka) Lv.																																							635	655
小倉 Kokura																																				618			652	
新下関 Shin-Shimonoseki																																				638				
厚狭 Asa																																				652				
小郡 Ogori																																		651		716			737	
徳山 Tokuyama																																		717						
新岩国 Shin-Iwakuni																														▲		610			735	741			812	
広島 Hiroshima								620								606						629	615	600	600		627		706	621		632	623		756		759			
東広島 Higashi-Hiroshima								644															637	613						646		659	641							
三原 Mihara																									708		721					731			813					
新尾道 Shin-Onomichi												612			618	639	636					739	654	643	725		740					745			818	825	818	832		
福山 Fukuyama								647				627		635	654	653	700			757		754	710	654	740		745				808	808		823	826	840	833	845		
新倉敷 Shin-Kurashiki								700				705	720				717			814		810	717	710	745				757							857	850	851		
岡山 Okayama							620	716		600	618	720											726	728	802		819		814	800	817	825	823			919	850	907		
相生 Aioi							644	733	707	617	635				724		748					848	747	757	839					845	834						919			
姫路 Himeji							651	748						743							858		802		853	853				841						928		945		
西明石 Nishi-Akashi							704	805	725					816									849	806					901			918		925						
新神戸 Shin-Kobe							721	816						830								906		834					930								1002			
新大阪 Shin-Osaka			617				725	823		707		705		850	830		806					927	905	852	905				959									1034		
京都 Kyoto			630				738	836		720		720		907	850	831	834				934	944	923	934	923				1018									1056		
米原 Maibara			647				751	846						921								959	940						1031											
岐阜羽島 Gifu-Hashima			703		708		804	854						938	907							1011	957		1009				1047											
名古屋 Nagoya	625	700	714	708	722		816	914		724	743		857	956	917	905	906		845		942	1023	1010	934					1057			911	925			928		1111		
三河安城 Mikawa-Anjo	635		718	722	738		825			743					926						956	1028	1023						1110											
豊橋 Toyohashi	645	710	727	734	754		833			816												1042	1032						1120											
浜松 Hamamatsu	655	720	738	744	804		858			850												1100							1134											
掛川 Kakegawa	703		745	755	814					905																														
静岡 Shizuoka	705	738	753	806	825		914			923												1114																		
新富士 Shin-Fuji	721		803	816	845					940																														
三島 Mishima	721	756	810	821	852		938			956				1014								1128																		
熱海 Atami	753									1010																														
小田原 Odawara										1027																														
新横浜 Shin-Yokohama										1044																														
東京 Tokyo Ar.										1059																														

N ...... **Nozomi** (All seats reserved.) H ...... **Hikari** K ...... **Kodama** ☆ ...... Not running on Sundays and holidays

...... All seats in ordinary cars are unreserved during weekdays. However, some seats are reserved on Saturdays, Sundays and national holidays.

(a) Not running on Saturdays and holidays (b) Not running on Saturdays (except in case of Saturdays is holidays) (c) Not running on Saturdays and holidays

...... All cars are ordinary class and all seats are non-reserved.

★ ...... All seats in ordinary class are reserved. ...... All seats in ordinary class are non-reserved. ▲ (d) Running on Apr. 22~.

Table 10.3
Comparative statistics for Series 700 Train-Sets

Model	Series 700	Series 700E	Series 500
Electrical System	AC 25kV·60Hz	AC 25kV·60Hz	AC 25kV·60Hz
Configuration	12M4T	6M2T	16M
Nominal riding capacity	Ordinary: 1123 1st class: 200	Ordinary (non-res): 245 Ordinary (reserved): 326 1st class: nil	Ordinary: 1124 1st class: 200
Weight (tes/trainset loaded)	708	320 (tare)	688
Maximum Speed (km/h, mph)	285/177	285/177	300/186
Balancing speed on level (km/h, mph)	338/210	338/210	365/225
Starting acceleration (km/h/s) Tokai: Sanyo	1.60 1.96	1.60 1.96	1.60 1.92
Power control system	VVVF+IGBT	VVVF+IGBT	VVVF+GTO
Brake systems	AC regenerative + elec.actuated. air (T cars eddy current) Continuous control on adhesion pattern.	AC regenerative + elec.actuated. air (T cars eddy current) Continuous control on adhesion pattern.	AC regenerative + elec.actuated. air (T cars eddy current) Load response device Continuous control on adhesion pattern.
Body construction	Aluminum alloy Equipment underslung, interspersed with dummy plates.	Aluminum alloy Equipment underslung, interspersed with dummy plates.	Welded aluminum-alloy brazed honeycombe + extruded aluminium sections.
Body dimensions (m) Length x Width x Height End cars Intermediate car	27.10 x 3.38 x 3.65 24.50 x 3.38 x 3.65	27.10 x 3.38 x 3.65 24.50 x 3.38 x 3.65	26.75 x 3.38 x 3.69 24.50 x 3.38 x 3.69
Body dimensions (ft) Length x Width x Height End cars Intermediate car	88.9 x 11.1 x 12.0 80.3 x 11.1 x 12.0	88.9 x 11.1 x 12.0 80.3 x 11.1 x 12.0	87.7 x 11.1 x 12.1 80.3 x 11.1 x 12.1
Bogie	Wheel diam: 0.86m (33.9in.) Wheelbase:2.50m (8.2ft) Bolsterless, no end beams	Wheel diam: 0.86m (33.9in.) Wheelbase:2.50m (8.2ft) Bolsterless, no end beams	Wheel diam: 0.86m (33.9in.) Wheelbase:2.50m (8.2ft) High-speed, bolsterless
Traction motors	AC 3-phase cage, asynchronous TMT6 (TMT7) 48 motors/train-set 275 kW/369 h.p./motor 13 200 kW(17 694 h.p.)/train Force-ventilated	AC 3-phase cage, asynchronous WMT205 24 motors/train-set 275 kW/369 h.p./motor 6600 kW(8847 h.p.)/train Force-ventilated	AC 3-phase cage, asynchronous WMT204 64 motors/train-set 275 kW/369 h.p./motor 17 600 kW (23 592 h.p.)/train Force-ventilated
Gear ratio	1:2.98 (23:68)	1:2.79 (28:78)	1:2.79 (28:78)
Auxiliary power	Stationary-voltage stabilizer AC-DC100V Aux. transformer AC100V Tertiary winding AC 440V	Stationary-voltage stabilizer AC-DC100V Aux. transformer AC100V Tertiary winding AC 440V	Stationary-voltage stabilizer AC-DC100V Aux. transformer AC100V Tertiary winding AC 440V
Pantograph/current collector	TPS301 (Single-arm) 2 pantographs/train-set	WPS205 (Single-arm) 2 pantographs/train-set	WPS204 (Wing-shaped) 2 current collectors/train-set

Source: JR-C, JR-W

Left: Extracts from 2000 timetable for the Tokaido and Sanyo Shinkansen: the down evening services from Tokyo (far left) and the early morning eastbound ones from Kyushu and western Honshu (right).

opened up for attention. A high-speed computer monitoring system continuously provides the driver and conductor with information on the operation of the on-board equipment. Data is also recorded, and an automatic testing system enables maintenance effort to be optimised.

The maximum speed on the Tokaido Shinkansen remains at the present 270 km/h. This is because the pioneering line was designed for lower speeds than the subsequent Shinkansen. Another factor that has to be taken into account is the frequency of the service, as speeding up a few of the trains could make it difficult to fit in all the required slower services. As a result it is currently not cost-effective to push the speed up any higher.

On the other hand, the Sanyo Shinkansen has easier curves, a wider gap between the tracks, and major civil engineering structures which produce less noise. The Series 700 are, therefore, permitted to run at speeds of up to 285 km/h (177 m.p.h.) on JR-West's high-speed line, improving overall journey times for passengers west of Shin-Osaka, where the higher capacity of their regenerative braking system also makes them more efficient electri-

cally. The opening of the new Kansai Airport in 1994 has provided a new flow of international passengers, as JR-West operates a half-hourly, limited-express service over the 60.5 km (37.6 mile) Japanese-gauge link with the Shinkansen at Shin-Osaka, using their *Haruka* EMUs, which have received one of the Brunel international design awards.

The first Series 700 was unveiled in October 1997, and early in the following year it undertook extensive trials on the Tokaido and Sanyo Shinkansen. In March 1999 the trains entered commercial operations on the *Nozomi* workings between Tokyo and Hakata, sharing the operations with the Series 500s. JR-West has also introduced a 8-car version – *Hikari Rail Star* – for use west of Shin-Osaka, which does not include any Green Cars. These are used in place of the previously-operated 'short' trains of Series 0 stock, the latter vehicles now being confined to the *Kodama* services. JR-Central, on the other hand, withdrew its final Series 0 units in September 1999, ending the 35-year reign of the original 'Bullet Trains' on the route for which they were designed, although the only remaining examples of

Left: The pantograph and its shielding on the Series 700 Shinkansen are shown well in this photograph of a JR-West *Hikari Red Star*. *Mikio Miura*

Below: A line-up of JR-Central and JR-West Shinkansen at Tokyo Ooi Depot in October 1999. From left to right the sets are: Series 100, Series 300, Series 500, Series 700, 'Doctor Yellow' T2 and '300X'. *Mikio Miura*

the first batches of these cars were in museums! Technical details of the Series 700s are given in Table 10.3, together with those for the Series 500s.

The introduction of these new designs of rolling-stock has produced additional significant improvements for the travelling public, quite apart from their improved ambience and ride. The first obvious changes have been with the Shinkansen timetable. Two extracts from the JR-Group public version for 2000 are given on page 94. The first shows the eastbound evening peak from Tokyo, when 11 trains are scheduled to leave in the hour beginning with the departure of the 17.52 *Nozomi*. (The type of train is shown by the letter at the head of the timetable: N for *Nozomi*, H for *Hikari* and K for *Kodama*). Next after the 17.52 is another *Nozomi* for Shin-Osaka, which does not run on ordinary Saturdays, as shown by the (b) reference in the table. Then comes a *Hikari* for Hiroshima, which is followed by a *Kodama*, which, like many other such workings, only goes as far as Nagoya. (The intermediate stations between there and Shin-Osaka are frequently served by *Hikari*, as are many of those travelling beyond this city, although other westbound *Kodama* start there). Then come three more *Hikari* for Shin-Osaka, of which only the third makes the two 'classic' intermediate stops at Nagoya and Kyoto. The first calls additionally at Shin-Yokohama and the next solely at Gifu-Hashima.

At 18.31 there is another *Kodama* for Nagoya, followed by a *Hikari* for Shin-Osaka, which stops at Shin-Yokohama and all stations after Nagoya. The 18.42 *Kodama* travels no further west than Mishima, and is quickly overtaken by the 18.45 for Okayama, The last long-distance departure in the hour is the 18.52 *Nozomi*, the final through train of the day for Hakata. It is booked to arrive seven minutes before the midnight shut-down of the Shinkansen, having overtaken the previous *Hikari* to reach Nagoya no less than 19 minutes before it.

The second timetable abstract shows the beginning of the day's eastbound services, when the system recommences passenger activities at 06.00 each morning. As on all lengthy high-speed railways, trains have to be started at intermediate stations as the day begins, and it will be seen that the first two *Nozomi* commence their journeys at Shin-Osaka and Okayama, and the next pair at Osaka and Hiroshima.The timetable also includes trains which do not run on Sundays, shown by (a) in the column

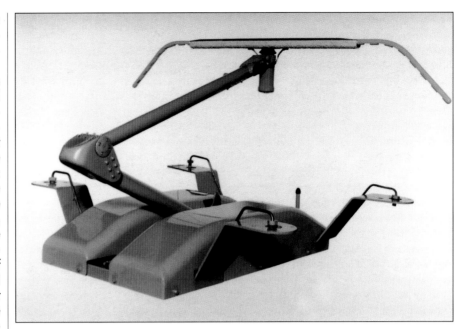

Top: Single-arm pantograph of Series 700 train.

Centre: Interior of Series 700 Green Car.

Bottom: Self-service drinks and food cabinets on Series 700 train.

JR-C (3)

concerned. The first such train is the 06.18 *Hikari* from Shin-Osaka, which, on weekdays reaches Tokyo 14 minutes after the 06.00, having been overtaken at Nagoya by the *Nozomi* which leaves Osaka between them.

When first introduced, the *Nozomi* services worked by the Series 300s ran at hourly intervals from Tokyo to Shin-Osaka, and it was not until the following year that they were extended to run for most of the day covering the full length of the Tokaido and Sanyo Shinkansen between Tokyo and Hakata. In the 2000 timetable the *Nozomi* are frequently scheduled in pairs, with the workings now in the hands of the Series 500s and 700s. From Tokyo, for example, 'N 21' leaves at 15.56, running all the way to Hakata, and is followed by 'N 59' four minutes later, for Shin-Osaka, each of them making the normal two intermediate stops at Nagoya and Kyoto. There is a corresponding pattern in the eastbound direction, with a *Nozomi* setting off from Shin-Osaka three minutes ahead of the one which has started just over 2 hours earlier from Hakata. The latter sometimes makes a call at Shin-Yokohama, getting into Tokyo Central seven minutes after the train ahead, instead of the usual three-minute gap.

Another feature of the present services shown in the abstract is the morning commuter service into Tokyo. The first eight arrivals, between 07.21 and 08.52 are all *Kodama*, five of them coming from Mishima, two from Hamamatsu and the other from Shizuoka. It is, of course, not merely a coincidence that there are rolling-stock depots and a workshop at the first two locations! In this country too, as passengers took advantage of high-speed travel, BR based virtually all its InterCity 125 fleets away from London.

Loadings on these Tokyo commuter Shinkansen services are extremely heavy, as land values have forced up the value of housing. Anyone wanting to buy a house valued at five times their annual salary will not be able to do so within 30–40 miles of the capital city. To cover this distance on a commuter line can involve up to 2 hours' travelling each way, so the prospect of journeying the 50-odd miles (84 km) from Odawara, for example, by Shinkansen in less than 40 minutes is very attractive. As those who participated in the *Zadankai*, which the writer chaired in Kyoto in 1994, heard, this was leading to unacceptable crowding on these services, with JR-Central giving reductions of 40–60% on season tickets.

Table 10.4 gives the details of the these services, excluding the seasonal trains, and it will be seen that the overall total has now risen to 435, an increase of 13% over the figure given in Table 8.7. When the two are compared in more detail, several interesting things become apparent. The totals of daily *Nozomi* and *Kodama* workings have increased by 42 and 24% respectively, whereas the number of *Hikari* services has actually dropped by five. These changes reflect the growth areas in longer-distance and commuting services, as mentioned earlier, and it is noteworthy how the two railways have been able to recast their timetables to meet these requirements.

It might be thought that all these additional services would require a larger rolling-stock fleet. However, Table 10.5, which lists the totals of Shinkansen coaches owned by JR-Central and JR-West between 1996 and 2000 shows this is not the case. In spite of the former's increased numbers of Series 300 and 700 trains, their overall total has dropped by nearly 6% since 1996, and JR-West has reduced its fleet size by 2%. A lot of this will have resulted from the shorter journey times, enabling trains to travel longer distances during the working day, but the newer designs may also require less time for servicing and overhaul.

The 1997 and 1999 World Speed Surveys produced by *Railway Gazette International*, showed there were also significant increases in the performance of the fastest trains on the Tokaido and Sanyo Shinkansen, the latter, with its new top speed of 300 km/h, taking the lead. As shown in Table 10.6, the two *Nozomi* which averaged 261.8 km/h (152.7 m.p.h.) between Hiroshima and Kokura in 1997 had increased to a total of no less than 12. As far as fastest journey times are concerned, Table 10.7 shows that in 1999 one *Nozomi 500* averaged no less than 242.5 km/h (150.7 m.p.h.) over the full length of the Sanyo Shinkansen, inclusive of three intermediate stops. Another eight of the *Nozomi 500* services running the whole way between Tokyo and Hakata average 220.0 km/h (136.7 m.p.h.) overall, including six or seven intermediate stops – an amazing performance over such a distance.

None of these changes have been to the detriment of punctuality. In Chapter 8 we looked at the Tokaido Line's performance up to 1996, and Table 10.8 takes the story on to 1999. That year the 'Annual Average Deviation from

Table 10.4
Daily Numbers of Trains on Tokaido and Sanyo Shinkansen, 2000
(Regular service trains, Mondays to Fridays, including seasonal scheduled trains)

	Nozomi	Hikari	Kodama	Total
WESTBOUND				
Tokaido Line only	8	32	38	78
Through services	17	35	-	52
Sanyo Line only	1	20	67	88
TOTALS	**26**	**87**	**105**	**218**
EASTBOUND				
Tokaido Line only	10	30	41	81
Through services	16	36	-	52
Sanyo Line only	2	19	63	84
TOTALS	**28**	**85**	**104**	**217**
GRAND TOTALS	**54**	**172**	**209**	**435**

Source: JR-Central, JR-West

Table 10.5
Tokaido & Sanyo Shinkansen: Numbers of Coaches 1996–99

Tokaido Shinkansen

			Series		
Year	0	100	300	700	TOTAL
1996	542	912	576	-	2 021
1997	384	848	720	-	1 952
1998	240	800	912	16	1 968
1999	64	800	976	80	1 920
2000	0	752	976	176	1 904

Source: JR-C

Sanyo Shinkansen

			Series				
Year	0	100	100N	300	500	700E	TOTAL
1996	522		144	144	-	-	826
1997	453	80	144	144	16	-	837
1998	311	112	144	144	96	-	807
1999	263	112	144	144	144	-	807
2000	211	96	144	144	144	72	811

Source: JR-W

Table 10.6
Fastest Shinkansen Start-to-Stop Speeds: 1997–1999

Year	Train	From[1]	To[1]	Distance km	miles	Time min	Speed km/h	mph
1997	2 *Nozomi 500*	Hiroshima	Kokura	192.0	119.3	44	261.8	162.7
1999	12 *Nozomi 500*	Hiroshima	Kokura	192.0	119.3	44	261.8	162.7

[1] Some of the journeys were in the opposite direction.

Source: *Railway Gazette International*.

Table 10.7
Fastest Shinkansen Journeys, 1997–1999

Year	Train	From	To	Distance km	miles	Time hr	min	No. of Stops	Speed km/h	mph
1999	1 *Nozomi* 500	Shin-Osaka	Hakata	553.7	344.0	2	17	3	242.5	150.7
1999	8 *Nozomi* 500	Tokyo	Hakata	1069.1	664.3	4	49	6/7[2]	220.0	136.7

[2] One journey made seven stops, the others six.

Source: *Railway Gazette International*.

Schedule' for the Tokaido Shinkansen was just 0.4 minutes (24 seconds), a remarkable figure, but it had actually slipped slightly since the previous year. Unlike the British Intercity margin of 10 minutes before a train is even considered as being late, the JR-C figure is the average of the total time of late departures and arrivals at Tokyo and Shin-Osaka of more than one minute. All delays are included, even those 'caused by uncontrollable reasons such as heavy rain, typhoons and heavy snowfalls'.

The Japanese railways make great use of train graphs. They are a particularly useful tool with single lines, and the story is told that in the early days Japanese railwaymen were impressed by how quickly their English managers were able to recast a timetable after retiring to the privacy of their office. In due course they discovered that train graphs were being used, since when they have become a vital tool, even with lines so highly automated as the Shinkansen.

From our point of view they also provide a graphic indication of how traffic has grown on the system, as can be

Table 10.8
Tokaido Shinkansen: Train Punctuality 1996–1999

Year (ending 31 March)	Average Lateness (seconds)
1996	53
1997	36
1998	18
1999	24

seen from a comparison of part of the 1964 and 2000 graphs on page 100. The different stations are shown down the left-hand margin, with Tokyo at the top and Shin-Osaka at the bottom. Time forms the horizontal scale, so lines representing trains travelling from Tokyo slant downwards from left to right, while those in the other direction rise upwards. Each line is identified by the appropriate train number. The straight visual comparison tells the whole story of how traffic has grown in just over 31½ years.

Finally it is worth comparing fare levels on the Tokaido Shinkansen with those on 'Britain's Fastest Railway', the East Coast route. Table 10.9 lists the range of ordinary Shinkansen fares between Tokyo and Osaka with the Open First and Open Second ones from King's Cross to Alnmouth. The actual Japanese journey covers 320.3 miles (515.4 km), although the tariff distance is longer. The UK journey quoted is for the nearest comparable distance available by Intercity trains, which is 303¼ miles (488.0 km). It should be stressed that the Japanese revenue structure starts with a basic fare determined by the distance travelled, and this is increased by various supplements. British Intercity ticket costs are not related directly to distance, and the most expensive are the 'Open' fares. Then there are various cheaper offers, such as 'Savers' and 'APEX tickets', with different restrictions on times and days when they are available. The fairest comparison with the Japanese ones is thus to quote the full 'Open' fares. It will be seen that, on this basis, the lowest Shinkansen fares are less than ours per mile, and even first-class on the *Nozomi* is less expensive than on the Great North Eastern Railway. It is very interesting to compare these figures of 2000 with those for 1995/96 quoted in the first edition of this book. During the intervening years Japanese fares have increased by 2%, whereas the quoted ones for this country rose by 16-17%!

Table 10.9
Fares for single Tokyo–Osaka Shinkansen journey, 2000 (Normal season)

	Yen	Yen/mile
Basic fare	8 510	27
By ordinary Shinkansen		
Unreserved	13 240	41
Reserved	13 750	43
Green Car	18 390	57
By 'Nozomi'		
Reserved	14 720	46
Green Car	19 360	60

Source: JR-C

In the Series 100 trains, the double-deck Green Cars have small 1 to 4-seater cabins on the lower level, which attract an additional supplement.

Fares for single King's Cross–Alnmouth journey, Spring 2000

	£	Yen	Yen/mile
Standard Open	77.50	10 560	42
First Open	113.00	15 520	61

Source: National Rail Enquiries

For April 2000 exchange rate of £1 = 163 Yen has been used.

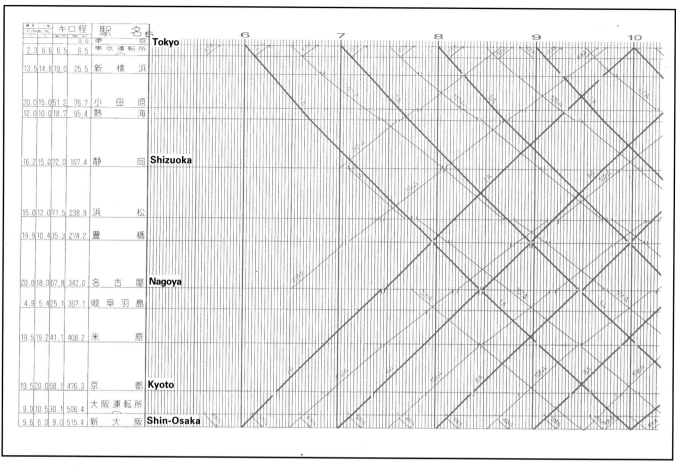

Above: Train diagram for 1964 Tokaido Shinkansen services, with one *Hikari* and one *Kodama* each way per hour.

Below: Train diagram for Tokaido Shinkansen services in 2000, with up to 11 departures from Tokyo in an hour.

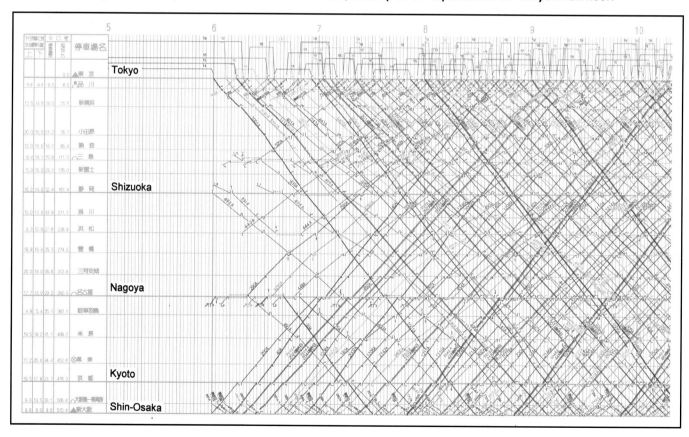

CHAPTER 11
Maglev & the Chuo Shinkansen

For many years research has been taking place throughout the world on how to achieve high-speed land-travel with vehicles suspended above the ground, either by magnetic fields or an air-cushion. Numerous such ideas were put forward in the early 1960s, before the start-up of the Tokaido Shinkansen had shown what could be achieved with steel-wheel-on-steel-rail. Amongst the many organisations which carried out investigations into magnetic-levitation were JNR, the Railway Technical Research Institute, and Japan Air Lines. The last-named was particularly interested in a fast link between Tokyo and the new international airport at Narita.

As shown in Table 11.1, Japanese research on linear-motors for railways began in 1962, and eight years later fundamental work was started on test equipment for super-conducting electro-magnets. Two years later they achieved 'lift-off' with the first test car, ML-100, in the Institute's grounds at Kokubunji, on the western outskirts of Tokyo, this vehicle running on an inverted T-shaped track. Although research work still continues at this location, in the 1970s a full-scale Test Track was constructed near Mimitsu station, in Miyazaki Prefecture, on the east coast of the island of Kyushu. The workshops, etc were at one end, and the elevated track

ran for 7 km (4.3 miles) generally parallel to the '1067mm-gauge' railway, with the electrical 'power-conversion' station and observation point situated close to Higashitsuno station. The facility was opened in April 1977, and, over the next two decades, numerous images of various maglev vehicles speeding their way along the shores of the Pacific Ocean appeared in the world's technical press as well as in 'Tomorrow's World' on BBC Television.

Still using T-shaped track, in 1979 vehicle ML-500 achieved a world record of 517 km/h (321.3 m.p.h.). The central beam of the track divided the vehicle almost in half, and there was no way in which a commercial design could be based on such an arrangement. If anyone had imagined otherwise, the historic problems of the Listowel & Ballybunion Railway in southern Ireland would have quickly disillusioned them! For the initial maglev experiments, however, it was a logical configuration, and the 1979 record completed the work with this layout.

A change was then made to a U-shaped guideway, and further tests were carried out with two different vehicles, MLU001 and MLU002, many of them being manned. Unfortunately the latter unit caught fire during a test run in

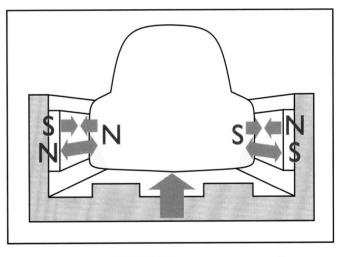

Above left: The first Japanese maglev test car, ML-100, on its T-shaped track in the grounds of the Railway Technical Research Institute at Kokubunji.   *JR-Central*

Above: Diagram of cross-section of the side-wall maglev system showing how levitation forces are generated during high-speed forward movement.   *JR-Central*

Left: The first U-beam maglev unit, MLU001, in its two-car form, races along the Miyazaki Test Track in Kyushu. It eventually reached 249.0 m.p.h. (400.8 km/h).   *JR-Central*

1991, but the reasons for this were quickly pinpointed. It was rebuilt as MLU002N, which finally achieved a speed of 431.0 km/h (267.8 m.p.h.) unmanned in 1994, and, in the following year went almost as fast (411.0 km/h, 255.4 m.p.h.) in manned condition.

Back in 1989 a decision had been made by JR-Central to build a full-size test track in Yamanashi Prefecture, north of Mount Fuji. This was situated on a route that could well be developed into a future commercial maglev line. For some time the Japanese government had been concerned with the way the country was developing, and was anxious to reverse the trend towards centralisation in the Tokyo area. It wished to relocate vital economic functions and governmental organisations to outlying regions, but in these new locations they would need good transport connections with the capital, in the same way as has happened with the UK's National Health Headquarters moving to Leeds.

By 1991 the Tokaido Shinkansen was, however, already reaching saturation at peak periods, as shown in Figure 11.1. Surveys of the non-reserved seat loadings on *Hikari* trains between Odawara and Shizuoka showed they were averaging 92% of capacity throughout the day. For two hours in the morning all seats were filled, with loadings climbing to a maximum of 114% of capacity. There was a similar evening peak, which was longer, although not so intense. Imposing a whole new passenger flow on this would not 'create an affluent society of the 21st century, by helping to solve the problem of over-centralization in the Tokyo area and by promoting the preservation of the environment', to quote the Linear Chuo Express Construction Promotion Federation.

There were other considerations as well. For more than 30 years now, the Tokaido Shinkansen infrastructure has been at the receiving end of more and more trains, thundering along at increasing speeds. Inevitably the time is going to come when some of the major structures will need extensive repair or replacement, which will inevitably upset the tight scheduling. Japan also suffers extremes of weather, and the Tokaido Shinkansen traverses a corridor which is especially prone to earthquakes. The potential threat was made all too obvious by the Great Hanshin Earthquake in January 1995. Although its epicentre was just clear of the Tokaido Shinkansen, and JR-West worked wonders to get the afflicted stretch of their Sanyo Shinkansen back into commission, it was nevertheless out of action for nearly three months. The reconstruction of Kobe's expressways was a much longer job, and was not completed until September 1996.

In the light of all these considerations, in 1990 the Ministry of Transport directed Central Japan Railway and Japan Railway Construction Public Corporation to begin topographical and geological surveys for the Chuo Shinkansen between Tokyo and Osaka. The broad plans have since emerged, with the eastern end passing north of Mount Fuji, through the Kofu area, before swinging south to Nagoya. West of this point the new route would run south of the existing high-speed one, serving the ancient capital of Nara instead of Kyoto, before terminating in Osaka, Japan's second commercial city.

This route included the stretch adopted for the Yamanashi Maglev Test Line, and details were announced in 1992. The longitudinal profile in the illustrations shows the entire 42.8 km (26.2 mile) facility, but only the 18.4 km (11.5 mile) Priority Section has been completed so far. The whole of this area is fairly mountainous, and most of the twin 'tracks', known as guideways, are in tunnel, but a 'representative' viaduct is also included – a most attractive-looking structure close to the Control Centre. The route was laid out for speeds of up to 500 km/h (311 m.p.h.), so the sharpest curves have radii of 8 km (5 miles), a considerable increase from the 2.5-km (1.5-mile) ones on the Tokaido Shinkansen.

Maglev cars are light, and do not rely on physical adhesion for braking or acceleration, so gradients of up to 1 in 25 can be accommodated. The twin guideways, which are of the sidewall type, are set with their centres 5.8 metres (19 feet) apart. This is considerably wider than the corresponding 4.3 metres (14ft 1¼in) used with the Standard-gauge tracks for the Sanyo and all subsequent Shinkansen. The tunnels at floor level are 12.6 metres (43ft 4in) wide, and the maximum width of viaducts, including the exterior walkways, is 100 mm (4 in) more. The internal height of the tunnels is 7.7 metres (25ft 3in).

The Technology of Magnetic Levitation

There are two basic ways of achieving magnetic levitation. The first is the electro-magnetic type, and was used for the short link between Birmingham International railway station in the UK and the nearby airport terminal. In 1984 it was the first such system to come into service anywhere in the world, but was abandoned in June 1995 because of escalating maintenance costs due to the difficulty of getting spare parts.

The Birmingham cars achieved levitation by means of four electro-magnets which were held in position underneath the guideway (the maglev equivalent of a railway track) by brackets attached to the vehicle. At rest the cars sat on top of this steel guideway, but were lifted off it by switching on the magnets, which were then attracted upwards. However, because magnetic forces increase as the gap closes, a sophisticated, rapid-action, control system was needed to vary the current through the electromagnets to maintain the separation of 15 mm (0.6 in) required to enable the linear motor to move the car horizontally. A similar arrangement was to have been used with the much faster German 'Transrapid' system which was considered for the Hamburg–Berlin link, but that proposal was finally abandoned in early 2000.

A very different electro-*dynamic* arrangement is used in Japan, but these systems have the disadvantage that they only work when the vehicle is moving at speed. This means that a retractable, wheeled, 'undercarriage' is needed to support and guide the vehicle until it has accelerated sufficiently for the repulsive force to build up between its magnets and the equipment on the guideway. In its simplest form, the electro-magnets in the vehicle pass over a series of loops containing a continuous series of wire coils fixed to the base of the guideway. The moving magnetic field induces a current in each coil as it passes. As determined by Lenz as long ago as 1835, the current in the coil flows in such a direction as to oppose the change which is giving rise to it. In the case we are considering, this means that the magnetic field produced by the coil is of the same polarity as the magnet, which thus creates a repelling force between them. Provided this can be made large enough, the vehicle levitates.

At first sight it can appear confusing where the energy to do this comes from, even though the actual amount required is extremely small. As a magnet approaches a coil, the repulsive force slows the vehicle down slightly, but after passing over it, the repulsion speeds up the vehicle again, in theory by exactly the same amount. In practice, because there are some slight losses in the coil due to its electrical resistance, the exit speed is not exactly equal to

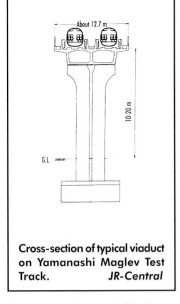

Cross-section of typical viaduct on Yamanashi Maglev Test Track. **JR-Central**

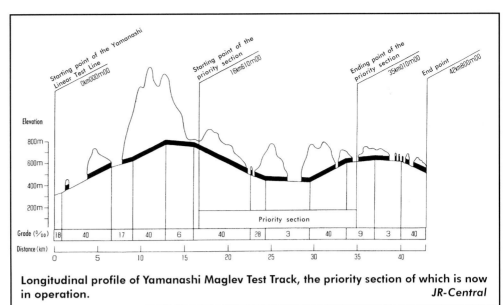

Longitudinal profile of Yamanashi Maglev Test Track, the priority section of which is now in operation. **JR-Central**

the approach one. This is made up by the thrust of the linear motor, as described below. It should not be forgotten that, as the magnetic fields from its coils produce the tractive effort needed to propel the cars, the coils experience equal and opposite forces so need to be securely fastened in the track.

For a high-speed commercial form of transport relying on levitation, the system also has to include a number of other features. The most important of these is lateral guidance. The Japanese have therefore adopted the sidewall system, with electro-magnets situated on the sides of the vehicle, and the coils on both sides of the track. The magnetic forces increase if the vehicle gets closer to one sidewall while the repulsion on the other side decreases. By connecting the coils on opposite sides with the so-called 'Null Flux Wires', the application of the Lenz principle results in the vehicle stabilising itself an equal distance from each side of the track.

With a series of simple coils in the sidewalls, the repulsive force would entirely be in the horizontal direction, which would produce no levitation. To obtain levitation as well, a very clever arrangement has been adopted. The side coils are shaped as vertical figures-of-eight, which means that the top and bottom lobes develop opposite magnetic polarities when the magnets on the vehicles pass across them a few centimetres below the cross-over point. The lower lobes thus repel the vehicle's magnets upwards, while the upper lobes exert an attractive force on them. The effects of levitation and guidance are thus combined into the same system.

To obtain sufficient levitating forces needed for a commercial vehicle, very strong electro-magnets are required, which must also be light, because they are part of the vehicle's dead-weight, so they have to possess the ability 'to lift themselves up by their own boot-laces'. To achieve the strength of field needed, and to excite the required flow of current, it is necessary to take advantage of super-conductivity. Many metals lose their electrical resistance when their temperature is lowered close to 'Absolute Zero'. This is −273.15°C, which is when all atomic and molecular vibrations virtually cease.

On the Japanese vehicles the temperature of the niobium/titanium wire coils in their superconducting magnets are maintained at about −269°C by liquid helium. Currents of many hundreds of amps can then flow round the magnetic coils without making them warm up. Any slight

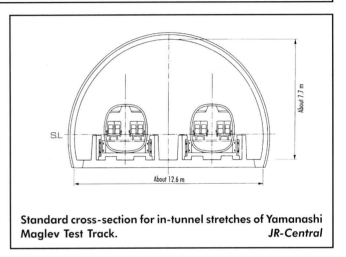

Standard cross-section for in-tunnel stretches of Yamanashi Maglev Test Track. **JR-Central**

production of heat causes the helium to boil, so 'GM-cycle' and 'Stirling-cycle' refrigeration is provided to reliquefy it. (Such items of equipment are widely used in the Magnetic Resonance Imaging equipment employed for medical diagnosis in hospitals). Careful design has enabled the amount of heat generated within each magnet to be cut to no more than 5 watts. This is inclusive of any that may 'leak' into the system from the vehicle or atmosphere.

Also included in the sidewalls of the Japanese system are the three-phase coils for the linear motors which provide the forward motion for the vehicle. These are the equivalent of the 'unrolled' stators of an ordinary traction motor, with the vehicle's magnets similarly forming the equivalent of the rotors. There is a difference, however, between the system adopted here and that used with most ac traction motors on trains. The Yamanashi system is the equivalent of a *synchronous* motor, instead of the usual asynchronous version. Only the second-generation TGVs and the SNCF 'Sybic' locomotives are fitted with synchronous motors.

By varying the frequency of the power supplied to the linear-motor's coils, the speed of the vehicle can be controlled, but there is an important difference between the synchronous and asynchronous varieties. In the latter the rotational frequency of the motor is slightly lower than the frequency of its power supply, the difference being known as 'slip'. With the synchronous variety the two match *exactly* at all times. This has the advantage in the case of the maglev system that it enables the position of the vehicle to be very accurately defined by controlling the speed.

Left: The prototype three-car unit, MLX01, in the depot on the Yamanashi maglev test line.
JR-Central

Right: In December 1996 alignment tests began on the Yamanashi maglev test line, with MLX01 being hauled at slow speed on its wheels by a diesel tractor.
Mikio Miura

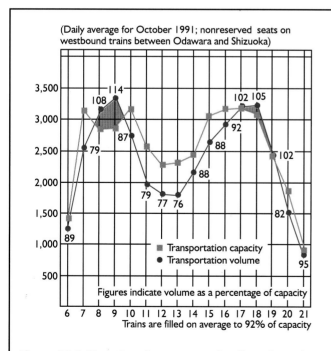

(Daily average for October 1991; nonreserved seats on westbound trains between Odawara and Shizuoka)

Figures indicate volume as a percentage of capacity

Trains are filled on average to 92% of capacity

- ■ Transportation capacity
- ● Transportation volume

Figure 11.1. Variations in passenger loadings throughout the day on Hikari trains between Odawara and Shizuoka, showing overloading in morning and evening peaks.
JR-Central

Above: Maglev running at 500 km/h (311 m.p.h.) in Hatsukari Tunnel on 28 November 1997
JR-C

Centre right: Five-car Maglev train passing Test Centre on 14 April 1999, the day it reached a maximum speed of 552 km/h (343 m.p.h.).
JR-C

Below right:The formal start of Maglev running at the Yamanashi Control Centre on April 1997.
Mikio Miura

Above: Speedometer in coach showing 552 km/h during test run on 14 April 1999. *JR-C*

Above: Turnouts on the Yamanashi Maglev Test line are somewhat complex affairs. *JR-C*

Motive power fitted with either of these types of motor generates its own variable-frequency supply for the motor coils, the control system matching the frequency with the speed selected by the driver. With the maglev cars their coils are fixed to the guideway, so the cars have to be operated from the Control Centre, rather than by someone on them. Video is used to give the controller an idea of the track ahead, but the system is, by and large, fully automated, so the progress of each 'train' is managed by a computer system, and on many of the test runs there was no-one aboard.

The idea of driving a full-sized train from the ground is not new, as the German high-speed railcars on the military railway between Marienfelde and Zossen in 1903 were operated in the same way, and they achieved speeds of up to 210 km/h (131 m.p.h.). In those days the man controlling them in the feeder-station would not have had anything like the same ability to know what was going on, which is probably why photographs of the generals in their spiked helmets observing the trials showed them looking so serious. Presumably, however, the train had a circuit-breaker to cut off the supply from their cumbersome triple side-wire supply system, as well as a brake, for use in an emergency.

With the Japanese system, the 'undercarriage' on the cars has to be lowered before the train slows down to the point where levitation is lost (about 160 km/h or 100 m.p.h.), and its wheels are provided with powerful brakes of the multiple-disc variety. These are designed to glow red-hot if used from high speed, but air-brakes, which extend from the cars' roofs like those on an aircraft, are also fitted. The sidewall propulsion coils can also be operated 'backwards' to give regenerative braking.

Table 11.1
Maglev Milestones

1962	Start of research on linear-motor propulsion for railways.
1970	Completion of fundamental test equipment for super-conducting magnetic levitation.
1972	Magnetic levitation achieved.
1977	Miyazake Maglev test track opened. Start of tests on inverted T-shaped track with ML-500 unmanned vehicle.
1979	World speed record of 321.3 m.p.h. (517.0 km/h) achieved with ML-500 vehicle.
1980	Tests began with MLU001 vehicle on U-shaped guideway.
1981	MLU001 reached 156 m.p.h. (251.0 km/h).
1982	Tests began with manned vehicle.
1986	Unmanned three-car unit reached 219.0 m.p.h. (352.4 km/h).
1987	Manned vehicle reaches 249.0 m.p.h. (400.8 km/h). Running tests began with MLU002.
1989	Decision made to build test line in Yamanashi Prefecture. MLU002 reaches 244.8 m.p.h. (394.0 km/h).
1990	Ministry of Transportation directs JR-Central and Japan Railway Construction Public Corporation to undertake studies of geography and geology for the Chuo Shinkansen between Tokyo and Osaka. Detailed route of Yamanashi Maglev Test line announced.
1991	Tests started on sidewall levitation system. MLU002 destroyed by fire during test run.
1992	Announcement made of 26.6 mile (42.8 km) test section of Yamanashi line.
1993	Running tests began with MLU002N vehicle on Miyazake test track. Outline details of Yamanashi test vehicle announced.
1994	Speed of 267.8 m.p.h. (431.0 km/h) achieved with MLU002N vehicle.
1995	New Japanese record of 255.4m.p.h. (411.0km/h) achieved with manned MLU002N. Prototype three-car MLX01 unit completed.
1997	Running tests commenced on Yamanashi Maglev Test Line in April with first trainset. Japanese manned record speed of 451 km/h (280 m.p.h.) achieved. Second trainset, with four cars, delivered to Test Track on 26 October. Unmanned world record speed of 531 km/h (330 m.p.h.) achieved with manned MLX01 on 12 December. Design speed of 550 km/h (342 m.p.h.) reached with unmanned MLX01 on December 24.
1998	Tests with two trains commenced on Yamanashi Test Track. Maglev trains pass successfully at combined speed of 966 km/h (600 m.p.h.) on December 17.
1999	Further world manned record of 552 km/h (343 m.p.h.) reached on 14 April. Passing speed of 1003 km/h (632 m.p.h.) achieved twice on 16 November with manned trains. Parents and children invited to travel on Maglev train at speeds of up to 451.9 km/h (281 m.p.h.).
2000	Five further years to research authorised. mid-June: total distance travelled on Yamanashi Maglev Test Line reached 89 173 km (55 409 miles).

In their normal operating mode, these Japanese vehicles have no physical contact with the guideway, so a means had to be found of supplying them with the power needed to meet their on-board demands, such as that required to run the lighting and air-conditioning. (The main super-conducting electro-magnets are excited before the train leaves the depot). This is achieved using a separate superconducting magnet, which induces current in the upper lobes of the levitation and guidance coils in the sidewalls. The current flowing in the lower loops in turn induces a flow in special loops mounted below this magnet on the side of the vehicle. These are not closed loops, but are connected to its electrical system, so their operation causes a drag on the vehicle, corresponding to the power being fed into the car. This has to be replaced by some of the energy being put into the guideway by the main propulsion supply from the power-conversion station, which maintains the car's speed. To keep the on-board equipment running when the vehicle is stationary, back-up batteries, and/or a gas-turbine generator, are provided. 'Leaky' cables on the tops of the sidewalls are used to transmit radio signals to and from the vehicle, so providing continuous two-way communication channels for speech and data transmission.

The first unit for trial running on the Yamanashi Maglev Test Line was the MLX01, a three-car set. It has four sets of superconducting magnets, mounted on the equivalent of bogies. Further sets of airbags support the body. The two central 'bogie' frames articulate the three cars together, and there are two separate ones at the outer ends.

As with the '300X' Shinkansen, two different nose profiles were tested on the prototype. At one end a double cusp shape is used, with an aero wedge at the other. The cars are 2.9 metres (9½ feet) wide and their actual height is 3.28 metres (10ft 9in). They leave the ground by 100 mm (4 inches) when fully levitated. The outer cars are 28 metres (92ft 10in) long, but the central one is much shorter at 21.6 metres (70ft 10in). Fully loaded with passengers the set weighs about 80 tonnes. Incorporated in the skin of the light-alloy monocoque bodies is a magnetic shield and an insulating layer. For lightness, the seats are plastics shells reinforced with carbon fibres, and are arranged in a 2+2 layout. Each pair has its own rectangular window, 400 mm high by 300 mm wide (15¾ in by 11¾ in), which is a lot larger than those on the average airliner.

'MLX01' is designed for a maximum speed of 550 km/h (342 m.p.h.), 10% higher than the projected service speed, which is the usual convention for trains and other guided forms of transport. At a cruising speed of 500 km/h (311 m.p.h.), a non-stop journey between Tokyo and Osaka should only take about an hour, which would be a remarkable cut from the present best time of 2½ hours. The unit was delivered to the Yamanashi Maglev Test Line in 1995, and was followed in 1997 by a second set, which consisted of four cars, one of which was 2.7 m (8.9 feet) longer than the single intermediate car in the first train, permitting the installation of three extra rows of seats.

Other changes in design were incorporated into this second set, the superconducting magnets being resiliently mounted, with an extra air-spring between them and the 'bogie', as well as between the bogies and car body. A better inductive power-collection system was installed in the leading car at the eastern end. With both sets the two end vehicles have different profiles, as was adopted with the '300X' Shinkansen, to determine the varying aerodynamic effects of the 'Aero-wedge' and 'Double-cusp' designs. In the case of the maglev units, the position of the

Table 11.2
Japanese Maglev Vehicles

Number	Date Built	Purpose
ML-100	1972	First T-shaped beam test vehicle with super-conducting magnet. Achieved levitation in grounds of Railway Technical Research Institute at Kokubunji.
ML-500	1976/77	T-shaped beam unit for trials on Miyazake Track.
MLU001	1980	First U-beam design for Miyazake Track. Also tested as two- and athree-car set.
MLU002	1987	Tested on Miyazake Track, but destroyed by fire during test run in 1991.
MLU002N	1992	Test vehicle for Miyazake Track, rebuilt from MLU002.
MLX01	1995	Prototype three-car unit for Yamanashi Test Line with sidewall levitation.
MLX01	1997	Second unit delivered to Yamanashi Test Line, with four cars, including stretched intermediate one. Length 24.3m. compared with 21.6m.(79.7 and 70.9 ft. respectively)

Source: JNR, JR Railway Technical Research Institute, JR-C.

two shapes in the sets has been reversed, to enable comparisons to be made as the two similar ones pass at speed. Arrangements were made to enable the second set to be 'strengthened' with one of the cars from the first, and it achieved its fastest speeds with a five-car formation.

Running tests with the first set began in April 1997, and on 12 December that year it reached a record 531 km/h (330 m.p.h.) with staff aboard, the maximum being achieved inside Takagawa Tunnel. Twelve days later, it twice achieved its design speed of 550km/h (342m.p.h.), again in the tunnel, but this time running unmanned. On the first of these runs, a hand-held video recording was made of the internal speedometer, from which the author was able to analyse the final acceleration, as shown in Table 11.3.

Zero was taken at the time speed reached 444 km/h (276 m.p.h.), and less than 20 seconds later the record had been achieved. It seems amazing that speed increased by 87 km/h (54 m.p.h.) in less than 20 seconds. However, in that time the unit travelled more than a mile and a half, so the simple increase in speed with distance is not unduly different from what is achieved by conventional trains starting from rest. However, as the energy in a moving object is proportional to the *square* of its speed, a far greater power input is needed at the velocities achieved by a maglev. Knowing the weight of the train it is possible to work out the power needed to achieve this acceleration, and those figures are also included in the table. They exclude the power needed to overcome air resistance.

On 15th April 1999 a new world speed record was achieved *twice* on the same day with a train of five cars. There were 13 of the project team aboard on each occasion when the speed of 552 km/h (343 m.p.h.) was reached, as before, in Takagawa Tunnel. The use of electronic timing equipment was vital to determine speeds such as this, because the maximum speed was only maintained for three seconds. With only the 18 km (11½ miles) of the Priority Section available, speeds such as this could clearly not be maintained for very long!

The next vital test was to determine the effect of two trains passing each other at a closing speed of 1000 km/h (621 m.p.h.), and these commenced in 1998. On December 17 a combined speed of 966 km/h (602 m.p.h.) was achieved, and in the following November the maximum

Table 11.3
Yamanashi Maglev Test Track

Train: MLX01
Date: 12 December 1997

Time secs	Speeds km/h	mph	Power required h.p.	kW
0.00	444	276	-	-
5.05	470	292	23 604	17 609
7.20	480	295	22 164	16 534
9.33	490	301	22 843	17 041
11.23	500	308	26 205	19 549
13.70	510	317	20 470	15 271
16.28	520	320	20 025	14 939
19.33	531	330	19 013	14 184
Average			22 046	16 447

was not only pushed up to 1003 km/h (623 m.p.h.), but this was achieved twice on the same day. The trains passed on the Ogatayama Bridge, and both were manned. The two units were not running at identical speeds, that on the north track travelling at 546 km/h (339 m.p.h.) while the other was appreciably slower at 457 km/h (284 m.p.h.).

In March 2000 the Maglev Technological Practicality Evaluation Committee, established by the Japanese Ministry of Transport, concluded that superconducting maglev technology could be a practical ultra-high-speed mass transport system. A further five years of research have been authorised, with the following aims:
1 To confirm the reliability and durability of the system by more running trials.
2 Carry out a study to reduce total costs.
3 Improve the aerodynamic performance of the rolling-stock.

Japan has by far the most experience with this form of transport. A speed of 517 km/h (321 m.p.h.) was achieved on the Miyazaki Test Track as long ago as 1979. This is faster than anything reached on rail, even by the record-breaking TGV-*Atlantique* unit at Vendôme eleven years later. In the course of the present larger-scale trials on the Yamanashi Maglev Test Line, as of 18 June 2000, a total of 89 173 km (55 409 miles) has been covered, and over 9000 passengers have been carried.

CHAPTER 12
The Shinkansen's Achievements and Significance

This book has chronicled the evolving story of the Shinkansen, and in conclusion it is now appropriate to take an overall look at its achievements relative to the other railways of the world.

At the time services began on the Tokaido Shinkansen in 1964, various other railway systems were also considering the possibilities of high-speed trains. For example, in the same year the 'Deltics' on the UK East Coast route began running at maxima of 100 m.p.h. (160 km/h). Initially this was only permitted over quite short distances, but during the 14 further years these locomotives remained in top-link service, a very high percentage of the 393 miles (632 km) between London and Edinburgh was passed for such a speed as the East Coast route was 'rebuilt by stealth.' These 3300 h.p. (2460 kW) diesel-electric locomotives were replaced by the diesel-electric InterCity 125 unit-trains, with their 125 m.p.h. (200 km/h) capabilities, but by that time the Tokaido Shinkansen had amassed no less than 13 years experience of running at 130 m.p.h. (210 km/h). Germany and France were somewhat quicker off the mark than Britain with speeds of over 100 m.p.h., but were still well behind Japan, where the concept of a dedicated high-speed line had been demonstrated, and its financial viability proven. The boost given to railway development worldwide by the Shinkansen was thus enormous.

Shorter journey times are one of the prime reasons which determine individuals' choice of transport mode, but these are specific to each traveller, and are consequently difficult for an outsider to compare. Average speed is, however, the reciprocal of journey time, and is a lot easier to comprehend, so it has become customary to quote these to show the relative standing of different railways throughout the world.

As mentioned in earlier chapters, *Railway Gazette International* publishes a two-yearly survey of world train speeds, and in 1989 the author was asked to see how start-to-stop speeds had changed since railways began to operate inter-city services from 1830 onwards. The resulting graph is given in Figure 12.1. The early data is inevitably incomplete, and the curve has been smoothed to show the general trends. Also included are a number of notable peak speeds achieved over short distances, and these are divided into two classifications. The dots represent speeds for standard rail vehicles, while the squares show those achieved by trains which could never operate commercially, such as the German military railcars with their three-phase side-contact masts, and the Garrett car with twin jet-engines mounted on its roof.

Right: A graph summarising how passenger numbers between Tokyo an Osaka have risen as journey times have decreased.
GEC-Alsthom

It will be seen that the world rail speed record for conventional trains has always been about twice the fastest start-to-stop commercial speed.

By 1850 the steam train was managing to achieve station-to-station averages of about 100 km/h (60 m.p.h.), and it was not until the 1930s that these averages began to rise during the 'Streamline Era', when diesel and electric traction was starting to supplant steam. Having reached another plateau of about 140 km/h (85 m.p.h.) by 1940, commercial speeds again levelled out, and it was not until the advent of the Tokaido Shinkansen that they again moved upwards, with start-to-stop schedules of over 100 m.p.h. (160 km/h) appearing for the first time.

The 1980s saw the completion of the first TGV lines, with the trains running at 270 km/h (169 m.p.h.) on the Paris-Sud-Est line after the first two years of service. They were followed by the 300 km/h (186 m.p.h.) *Atlantique* lines at the end of the decade. It was in 1990, just before the second of the routes that comprise the latter was opened, when a series of high-speed runs with TGV set No. 325 culminated in the present world rail speed record of 515.3 km/h (320.2 m.p.h.). The opening of the first French high-speed line pushed start-to-stop speeds up to 185 km/h (115 m.p.h.) by 1983, but the best Tokaido Shinkansen entry was only 4.1 km/h (2.5 m.p.h.) slower, and that Japanese line had 119 trains scheduled at more than 168 km/h (104 m.p.h.), whereas the French managed a mere 27.

By the mid-1980s, speeds in France had lifted start-to-stop averages over the 200 km/h (125 m.p.h.) level, and the fastest entry in 1985 was an average of 215.9 km/h (134.2 m.p.h.) between Paris and Mâcon, but the start of services on the Tohoku and Joetsu Shinkansen had also lifted Japanese speeds over the 200 km/h mark. That year the speediest of their 19 200+km/h schedules was the 206.7 km/h (128.5 m.p.h.) run by a *Yamabiko* between Koriyama and Omiya.

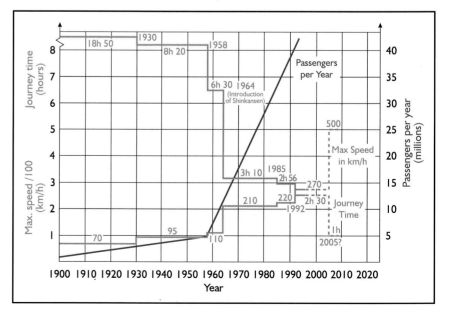

Although not shown on the figure, by 1991 the French service speeds had passed the 220 km/h (137 m.p.h.) mark, with a single run at 224.0 km/h (139.2 m.p.h.) between Paris Montparnasse and Le Mans on the *Atlantique* route. Again the Tohoku Shinkansen was not far behind, with six *Yamabiko* averaging 213.9 km/h (132.9 m.p.h.) between Morioka and Sendai. Two years later the French had pushed the best TGV *Atlantique* average to 245.6 km/h (152.6 m.p.h.), but in Japan the Sanyo Shinkansen took pride of place after the introduction of the Series 300 *Nozomi*, with a total of 27 trains in the two directions averaging 230.4 km/h (143.2 m.p.h.) between Hiroshima and Kokura. By 1995, with the opening of TGV *Nord Europe*, the SNCF had raised their best speed to exactly 250 km/h (155.3 m.p.h.), while the best Japanese start-to-stop averages on the Sanyo and Tokaido Shinkansen remained the same as they had been two years earlier.

The Europe/Asia comparison changed in 1997 with the introduction of the JR-West Series 500s, which could exploit their 300 km/h capabilities west of Osaka, and by the end of the 1990s station-to-station averages had gone up to 261.8 km/h (162.7 m.p.h.). Even more remarkable was the 1999 average of 242.5 km/h (150.7 m.p.h.) achieved between Shin-Osaka and Hakata, inclusive of three intermediate stops. Both these achievements were significantly ahead of the best the SNCF then had timetabled. Their fastest station-to-station speed at that time was 253.3 km/h (157.4 m.p.h.). In the first edition of this book the writer remarked that it would be interesting to see what transpired when the Series 500s and 700s made their debut, so the Japanese move into first place came as no great surprise to him.

It is worth considering how the Japanese Shinkansen have developed compared with the busiest British high-speed route, the main line out of London Euston to the West Midlands, Lancashire and Scotland. Although some work had obviously been done before the celebrated Japanese 1957 meeting in the Yamaha Hall, that conference started the public awareness of the proposals for the world's first high-speed railway. Seven years later commercial services began over the 320 mile (515 km) line between Tokyo and Osaka at speeds of up to 210 km/h (130 m.p.h.).

In the UK the BR Modernisation Plan was published in 1955, and included the electrification of some 326 miles (525 km) of what is now known as the West Coast route, the work being finished in 1967. Given that upgrading an existing facility is always slower than building from scratch, the time-scales and lengths of line are not dissimilar, so it is worth looking at the way in which the two systems have developed since. However, two important other points have to be taken into account - for much of its length the British line consists of quadruple track, and it has to handle local passenger services and freight trains in addition to the high-speed Intercity ones. On the other hand, the Old Tokaido and Sanyo Lines in Japan remain in operation, and, in effect, now form the equivalent of the 'Slow Lines' on the UK route.

Maximum speed on the reconstructed West Coast route was fixed at 100 m.p.h. (160 km/h), and it was only in the 1980s that parts of it were upgraded to 110 m.p.h. (177 km/h), neglecting the short-lived public services worked by the Advanced Passenger Train which had the ability to tilt on curves. Many of the original Class 86 electric locomotives are still in service, running at the same maximum speed of 100 m.p.h. or less, but in the mid-1970s these were sup-

plemented by the Class 87s. The latter design was upgraded to run at 110 m.p.h. in the 1980s, and later joined by the Class 90s with a similar capability. Much of the rolling stock still in use is also restricted to 100 m.p.h., with only the longer-distance trains running north of Crewe being formed entirely from Mk III coaches to enable the 110 m.p.h. capabilities of the faster locomotives to be utilised. Since Privatisation, however, Virgin Trains, with Railtrack, has embarked on a major upgrading to a maximum of 140 m.p.h. (225 km/h), but operations at this speed are still a few years into the future

When the original West Coast electrification was completed, an hourly service in each direction was introduced between Euston and Birmingham, with services further afield scheduled at no greater frequency. Even so, many more passengers were attracted by the faster and better trains, the 'sparks effect' lifting business by 70% in two years. By 1970 numbers had doubled compared with pre-electrification days. In Japan, within three years of the first full 12 months of operations on the Tokaido Shinkansen, passenger numbers had more than doubled from 31.0 to 65.9 million, and by 1995/96 the Tokaido total had increased to no less than 132.8 million – a further doubling.

Privatisation and the up-grading of the UK West Coast Main Line make it difficult to compare the services in the two countries today. However, on the Tokaido Shinkansen in 1996 there were 266 regular trains every day, with seasonal services lifting the average to 283. In 1995 the number of West Coast InterCity services operated in the UK was only 158 a day. Between 1964 and 1996 regular daily services on the Tokaido Shinkansen had risen from 60 to the figure of 266 mentioned above.

Moving on to 2000, there are now 263 regular trains running daily on the Tokaido Line. To arrive at the total for the whole of Japan, we must add the 172 similar daily workings on the Sanyo Shinkansen, together with 211 on the Tohoku Shinkansen, 95 on the Nagano route, and 56 on the Joetsu line. This gives a grand total of no less than 797 separate regular daily trains on the whole of that country's high-speed network. When one realises that in 1995 the combined total of InterCity expresses run daily by the UK West Coast, East Coast, Midland and Great Western Train Operating Companies only came to 444, the intensity of operation on the Japanese high-speed network can be appreciated.

Another important comparison has to be made between some of the largest traffic flows in different countries. In 1993 the following figures were included in Chris Green's presentation *InterCity Rail in Britain* at the 'Passenger Transport after 2000AD' conference held by the Royal Society.

	Passengers/year (millions)	Distances (miles)	(km)
Tokyo–Shin-Osaka	90	320	515
Paris–Lyon	20	279	449
London–Manchester	2	189	304

Source: *The Future of InterCity Rail in Britain*, BR

Building a completely new high-speed line between Manchester and London would not be justified by the additional passengers that were likely to be attracted to use the railway because of the reduced journey time. Nevertheless introducing faster trains on the existing tracks will give time savings, and, after the planned upgrade for the infrastructure, the use of tilting stock will improve the position further.

When the Tokaido Shinkansen was being built, the station at Yokohama was constructed in the open country outside the city. Such was the economic impulse produced by the high-speed railway that a major new conurbation has grown up around it. The two photographs show the station when new (top) and at present (bottom).

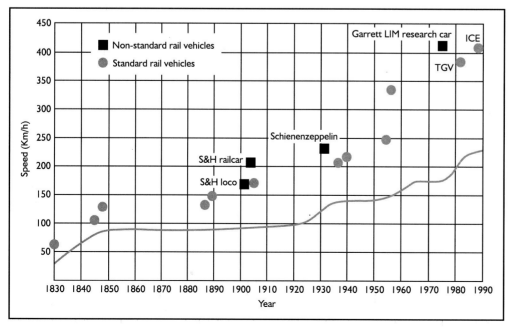

Figure 12.1 Diagram showing changes in start-to-stop speeds on the railways of the world between 1830 and 1990, together with notable maximum speed records.

Railway Gazette International

In the case of the Tokaido Shinkansen we have seen how journey times have been reduced from 3hr 10min with a service speed of 210 km/h (130 m.p.h.), to 2½ hours with the *Nozomi* running at 270 km/h (168 m.p.h.). JR-Central's announcement that the future Series 700 trains would not run faster than this on the Tokaido Shinkansen indicates that any increase would, under present circumstances, not be cost-effective on that route, bearing in mind the physical constraints. The Series 500s, however, began 300 km/h (186 m.p.h.) running on the Sanyo Shinkansen in 1997.

When making comparisons between the UK and Japan, it is important to realise how different are the distances between the main cities in the two countries. It is always difficult to be precise about the size of the population served by a particular station, but Birmingham considers itself as the UK's second city. New Street station in that city is only 113 miles from London Euston. By contrast, the distance from Tokyo Central station to Osaka, Japan's second commercial centre, is 320 miles. That is comparable to the distance between Euston and Ecclefechan (the closed station a few miles south of Lockerbie) on the West Coast main line, or between London King's Cross and Belford on the UK East Coast route. The number of inhabitants in either of these northern communities probably does not exceed 1% of the 2.5 million who live in Osaka. A comparable distance on the other British long-distance high-speed line, the Great Western route out of Paddington, would land one up 15 miles past the buffer-stops at Penzance, roughly five miles into the Atlantic, west of the Longships rocks off Land's End!

These comparisons with our own railway system enable us to see how the Tokyo - Osaka route was well-matched with the equipment designed for the Tokaido Shinkansen when it became the world's first high-speed railway. Earlier chapters have shown how the initial advantage secured by the railways in this way has been exploited subsequently, both in Japan and elsewhere in the world.

The safety record of the Japanese high-speed railways is outstanding, and, in conclusion, it is worth returning to the words of Hideo Shima, the 'father' of the Shinkansen. In 1994 he wrote a thoughtful article on the progress of the project he began almost 40 years earlier, which was published in the special edition of the *JR Tokai Technical Report* produced for the Tokaido Shinkansen 30th Anniversary celebrations in 1994. At the age of 93 he concluded with the following message to his railway readers:

'Finally, I have one last request. I hope that you'll always keep in mind that you have the lives of many passengers in your hands. This is not a light responsibility. Never forget it'.

His words make one realise how profound was his belief in the ability of 'Japan's New Network' to achieve standards no other railway or rival transport system could emulate, let alone surpass.

His death in March 1998 was marked by an obituary in *The Times* of London, which commented that he 'helped to create one of the most potent symbols of Japan's postwar reconstruction and emerging industrial might'. This fittingly combined a personal tribute with an acknowledgement of the national and international importance of the Shinkansen.

As this book was in the press in July 2000, it was announced that the Tokaido Shinkansen had received two prestigious international awards. The New York based Institute of Electrical and Electronics Engineers honoured the line as 'An Electrical Engineering Milestone', and the American Society of Mechanical Engineers designated the railway as 'A Landmark in Mechanical Engineering'. This was only the fourth time the two awards have been given to the same achievement, emphasising the high regard in which this pioneering high-speed railway is held by engineers throughout the world.

Above: The plaque recording the awards received by the Central Japan Railway.

Chronology

Date

<u>1870</u>
25 April   Surveying work began for first railway in Japan. Gauge of 3 feet 6 inches (1067mm) adopted by English engineers because of similarity of Japan's topography to that of New Zealand.

<u>1871</u>
September   First locomotives and coaches reached Japan.

<u>1872</u>
12 June   Regular daily services began between Shinagawa (Tokyo) and Yokohama.
14 October   Meiji Emperor attended opening ceremony and made round trip between Shinagawa and Yokohama.

<u>1873</u>
19 May   Official start of commercial train services.

<u>1874</u>
11 May   Regular services began between Osaka and Kobe.

<u>1875</u>   Construction of passenger coaches commenced at Kobe Works.

<u>1876</u>
5 February   Railway extended from Osaka to Kyoto.

<u>1877</u>   First Japanese locomotive drivers appointed.

<u>1880</u>   Railway extended through Osakayama Tunnel to Otsu.

<u>1889</u>
1 July   Railway between Shimbashi and Kobe via Osaka inaugurated – journey time between two termini just over 20 hours.

<u>1892</u>
June   Railway Construction Act passed, proposing a larger national network.

<u>1893</u>
March   1870 miles (3010 km) of railways in operation in Japan.
June   First locomotive constructed in Japan, by R.F. Trevithick at Kobe Works, using imported components.

<u>1895</u>
1 February   Kyoto Electric Railways began first Japanese commercial service using electric traction.
First complete locomotive constructed in Japan.

<u>1896</u>
September   Fastest Tokaido Line timings between Kobe and Shimbashi reduced to just over 17 hours.

<u>1903</u>
January   Tokyo–Kobe times by Tokaido Line reduced to 15 hours.

<u>1906</u>
16 April   Lightweight 'Super Express' of four coaches introduced on Tokaido Line, reducing Shimbashi–Kobe time to 13hr 40min. (27 m.p.h./44 km/h)
September   Nationalisation of privately-owned main lines began, creating the Japanese Imperial Railways. Some local railways remained in private ownership.
December   'Super Express' extended to Shimonoseki in western Honshu.

<u>1907</u>   4452 miles (7165 km) of nationalised railways being operated.

<u>1911</u>   Proposal to convert railways to Standard Gauge (4ft 8½ in or 1435 mm) defeated.

<u>1913</u>
August   Double track completed over full length of Tokaido Line.

<u>1914</u>
20 December   Tokyo Central station opened.

<u>1919</u>   6116 miles (9842 km) of nationalised railways being operated.
First electric locomotive constructed in Japan (ED40).

<u>1922</u>
April   Railway Construction Act proposed the building of 10 158 km (6312 miles) of new branch lines.

<u>1926</u>
17 July   Automatic couplers fitted to all freight wagons on single day, except in Kyushu, where the change-over took place on 20 July.

112

1927
30 December   First 'Underground' line opened in Japan between Ueno and Asakusa in Tokyo.

1930
1 October   Government Railways began operating bus services.
    Class C51 4-6-2 steam locomotives began hauling *Tsubame* ('Swallow') expresses between Tokyo and Kobe in 8hr 59min. (8hr 20min to Osaka).

1934   4.8-mile (7.804-km) Tanna Tunnel completed between Atami and Numazu: part of the improvements made to the Tokaido Line.

1940   Work began on Standard-gauge high-speed line in Honshu. Work stopped during Pacific War.

1941–45   Pacific War. Japanese railways suffered severe damage from bombing and naval bombardment.

1942
11 June   Under-sea Kanmon Tunnel completed between Honshu and Kyushu. (2.2 miles/3.6 km long).

1949
1 June   Japanese National Railways formed.

1956
19 November   Electrification of old Tokaido Line completed from Tokyo to Osaka.

1957
July   Japanese National Railways launched major investment study, including construction of Tokaido Shinkansen.

1958
19 December   Tokaido Shinkansen authorised.

1959
20 April   Formal start of work on Tokaido Shinkansen, at entrance to Shin-Tanna Tunnel.

1961
2 May   World Bank agreed to lend $80 million for construction of New Tokaido Line.
18 October   Whole route of Tokaido Shinkansen agreed.

1962
26 June   Trial running began on Kamonomiya Test Track section of Tokaido Shinkansen.
31 October   Speed record of 125 m.p.h. (200 km/h) attained on test track.
    Research began on use of linear-motor propulsion for railways.

1963
30 March   Shinkansen stock reached 159 m.p.h. (256 km/h) on test.

1964
10 April   Trial running commenced between Kamonomiya and Atami.
7 July   *Hikari* and *Kodama* names adopted for Shinkansen trains.
25 July   First Shinkansen test train ran from Tokyo to Osaka, taking 10 hours.
25 August   Test running of trains on *Hikari* timings began on Tokaido Shinkansen, with journey times of 4 hours, using ATC.
1 October   The 320 mile (515 km) Tokaido Shinkansen opened between Tokyo Central station and Shin-Osaka – the first purpose-built high-speed railway in the world. Thirty return trips/day operated with journey time reduced to 4 hours compared with 6½ hours by old line.
    Japan Railway Construction Public Corporation formed to build new railways, with aid of government finance.

1965
9 September   Construction of high-speed line from Shin-Osaka to Okayama authorised.
1 November   Fastest Tokyo - Shin-Osaka times reduced to 3hr 10min.

1966
12 June   Passengers carried by Shinkansen reach 50 million.

1967
16 March   Construction of Sanyo Shinkansen started between Shin-Osaka and Okayama.
13 July   Passengers carried by Shinkansen reach 100 million.
25 November   Sprinklers installed to cope with snowfall at critical sites.

1968
25 November   Japan Railway Construction Public Corporation announced plans for nation-wide Shinkansen network with total length of 2952 miles (4750 km).

1969
25 April   New station opened at Mishima, between Atami and Shizuoka.
12 September   Additional stretch of Sanyo Shinkansen authorised, extending high-speed line from Okayama to Hakata.
2 July   Two-car Type 951 prototype began trial running.

Above: The end of an era. The leading car of the last JR-Central Series 0 Shinkansen at Hamamatsu Depot three months after withdrawal.
Mikio Miura

Below: Less than a month after the start of service running with Series 700s, a set passes peach trees in blossom near Odawara.
Mikio Miura

1970
10 February	Work began on extension to Hakata, including 11.6-mile (18.7-km) tunnel under strait between Honshu and Kyushu.
25 February	All *Hikari* trains provided with 16-coach formations.
13 May	Law for the Construction of Nationwide High Speed Railways passed. Five lines allocated top priority, including link with new Tokyo International airport to be built at Narita.

1971
18 January	Basic proposals for Tohoku, Joetsu and Narita Shinkansen announced.
1 April	Directive issued to start work on Tohoku and Joetsu Shinkansen.
28 November	Construction work on Tohoku and Joetsu Shinkansen commenced.

1972
24 February	Series 951 test car set speed record of 177.7 m.p.h. (286.0 km/h).
15 March	Sanyo Shinkansen opened between Shin-Osaka and Okayama. Renewal of Tokaido Shinkansen track began using heavier rails. COMTRAC put into operation.
23 September	Passengers carried by Shinkansen reach 500 million.
14 October	Magnetic levitation (Maglev) tests started with ML100.

1973
1 May	Break-through of undersea Shin-Kanmon Tunnel for Sanyo Shinkansen connecting Honshu with Kyushu. (Length 11.6 miles/18.7 km).
29 July	All *Kodama* trains provided with 16-coach formations. First prototype of lightweight Shinkansen trains for Tohoku and Joetsu lines delivered, capable of 162 m.p.h. (260 km/h).

1974
1 February	Work began on Shinkansen linking Tokyo with new Narita airport, but project later abandoned.
1 October	Passengers carried by Shinkansen reach 750 million.

1975
28 January	Opening of Tohoku Shinkansen deferred from 1977 to 1979.
10 March	Sanyo Shinkansen opened between Okayama and Hakata.
5 May	Record number of 1 032 136 passengers carried in one day.

1976
25 May	Passengers carried on Tokaido Shinkansen reach 1 billion.
19 November	Replacement of original Series 0 trains began with new stock.

1977
26 July	Trial running began with ML500 on Miyazaki Maglev test track.

1978
20 May	Narita International Airport opened. Served by Standard-gauge (1435mm) trains operated by Keisei Electric Railway.
5 June	Trials of second Series 961 train began on Oyama test track.

1979
11 October	Financial difficulties cause *Kodama* trains to be reduced in length from 16 to 12 coaches. New type of dining car brought into service.
28 November	Series 961 train set first of three new Japanese records, culminating in a speed of 198.2 m.p.h. (319.0 km/h) on 7 December.
12 December	World record speed of 321.3m.p.h. (517.0km/h) achieved with unmanned Maglev vehicle on Miyazaki test track.

1980
	Work began on Omiya–Tokyo section of Tohoku and Joetsu Shinkansen.
11 September	Important legal ruling on train noise made in favour of JNR.
31 October	Trial running commenced on Tohoku Shinkansen.

1982
15 May	Loan of $80 million repaid to World Bank.
23 June	Public services started on Tohoku Shinkansen between Omiya and Morioka.
15 November	Public services began between Omiya and Niigata on Joetsu Shinkansen.

1983
June	JNR Restructuring Advisory Committee formed.
23 June	Tohoku Shinkansen opened for commercial services between Omiya and Morioka.
15 November	Joetsu Shinkansen opened for commercial service between Omiya and Niigata.

1984
3 April	Passengers carried on Tokaido Shinkansen reach 2 billion.

1985

14 March   Omiya–Ueno section of northern Shinkansen lines opened, and maximum speed on Tohoku Line raised to 149 m.p.h. (240 km/h) – journey times from Tokyo to Morioka and Niigata substantially reduced. Fastest Tokyo–Shin-Osaka timings reduced to 3hr 8min.

27 March   Series 100 trains for Tokaido and Sanyo Lines unveiled, with two double-deck cars in each set.

20 August   Prototype Series 100 train reached 143 m.p.h. (230 km/h) on Tokaido Shinkansen and then, on 2 September, attained 162 m.p.h. (260 km/h) on Sanyo Shinkansen.

1 October   Series 100 prototype entered public service.

1986

13 June   Fleet introduction of Series 100 trains on Tokaido Shinkansen.

28 October   Act for restructuring ('Privatisation') of JNR passed.

1 November   Maximum speed on Tokaido Shinkansen raised to 137 m.p.h. (220 km/h). Series 100 trains used on fastest services, reducing Tokyo–Shin-Osaka journey time to 2hr 56min. (The 21.00 from Tokyo, the 'Cinderella Express' had a schedule of 2hr 52min).

1987

4 February   Miyazaki Maglev MLU001 reached 249.0 m.p.h. (400.8 km/h) with passenger aboard.

1 April   JNR 'Privatised', with a Holding Company owning all the Shinkansen assets and leasing them to the three regional companies in whose areas they operated.

11 November   Work started on converting Ou Line from Fukushima to Yamagata to take 'Mini-Shinkansen' trains.

1988

13 March   Seikan Undersea Tunnel between Honshu and Hokkaido opened after 24-year construction period. The world's longest underwater tunnel, with a total length of 33.46 miles (53.85 km), of which 14.5 miles (23.35 km) are under the sea.

West Hikari services introduced on Sanyo Shinkansen.

Three new stations opened on Tokaido Shinkansen (Shin-Fuji, Kakegawa and Mikawa-Anyo)

1989

11 March   Maximum speed on Sanyo Shinkansen raised to 143 m.p.h. (230 km/h) with *Grand Hikari* expresses using Series 100N stock.

2 August   Work commenced on Hokuriku Shinkansen.

1990

6 February   Ministry of Transport directed Japan Railway Construction Public Corporation and (JR-Central) to begin surveys for Chuo Shinkansen, following different route between Tokyo and Osaka from the Tokaido Shinkansen. Magnetic-levitation system to be considered.

8 March   Prototype of Series 300 Shinkansen completed (later *Super-Hikari* and then *Nozomi*).

10 March   Maximum speed raised to 171 m.p.h. (275 km/h) at one point on Joetsu Shinkansen. This was in-tunnel and applied in one direction only, enabling JR-East to claim the fastest service speed in Japan.

Most *Hikari* schedules between Tokyo and Shin-Osaka reduced to 2hr 52min.

1 April   Shinkansen extended from Hakata to Hakata-Minami. Passengers carried over 5.3 miles (8.5 km) of low-speed line connecting Hakata main station with new rolling-stock depot.

23 June   Two-level cars added to *Yamabiko* trains on Tohoku Shinkansen.

1 July   JR-Central formed 300X project team.

7 July   Series 300 train reaches 169 m.p.h. (272 km/h).

14 November   Test running began on Ou Line with Series 400 'Mini-Shinkansen'.

28 November   Work commenced on Yamanashi Maglev test line.

20 December   Joetsu Shinkansen trains began running directly to Gala Yuzawa ski resort on spur from main line.

1991

26 February   Passengers carried on Tokaido Shinkansen reach 3 billion.

28 February   Series 300 train attained 202.4 m.p.h. (325.7 km/h) on the Tokaido Shinkansen between Maibara and Kyoto.

19 March   JR-East commenced *Narita Express* service ('Japanese-gauge' – 1067mm) linking airport with Tokyo, Shinjuku, Ikebukuro and Yokohama.

26 March   Series 400 'Mini-Shinkansen' attained 208.8 m.p.h. (336.0 km/h) between Echigo-Yuzawa and Urasa on Joetsu Shinkansen.

20 June   Tohoku and Joetsu Shinkansen trains extended from Ueno into Tokyo Central station.

4 September   Formal start of work on extension of Tohoku Shinkansen from Morioka to Aomori.

7 September   Formal start of work on Kyushu Shinkansen – a 'Super Express' route.

17 September   Formal start of work on Hokuriku Shinkansen between Karuizawa and Nagano, site of the 1998 Winter Olympics.

19 September   Series 400 set reached 214.4 m.p.h. (345.0 km/h) on Joetsu Shinkansen between Echigo-Yuzawa and Urasa.

1 October   Shinkansen system sold by Settlement Corporation to the three companies leasing the high-speed lines (East, Central and West Japan Railways).

December   Fastest trains on Tokaido Line using Series 300 units named *Nozomi* ('Hope').

1992

13 March	Work commenced on Akita Shinkansen.
14 March	Series 300 *Nozomi* ('Hope') sets began service at 168 m.p.h. (270 km/h) between Tokyo and Shin-Osaka, reducing journey time to 2½ hours. East Japan Railway's STAR21 high-speed test train completed.
1 July	Yamagata Shinkansen began regular service, using Series 400 'Mini-Shinkansen' running between Fukushima and Yamagata over track regauged from 1067mm (3ft 6in) after uncoupling from Series 200 trains on Tohoku Shinkansen.
8 August	West Japan Railway's WIN350 reached 217.7 m.p.h. (350.4 km/h) after achieving 214.9 m.p.h. (345.8 km/h) on 6 August and 188.3 m.p.h. (303.0 km/h) on 21 July.

1993

18 March	Series 300 *Nozomi* trains began hourly service in each direction between Tokyo and Hakata, with fastest journey time of 5hr 3min.
August	First shares for JR-East sold on Stock Market.
15 September	East Japan Railway's STAR 21 reached speed of 231.1 m.p.h. (372 km/h) on Joetsu Shinkansen.
21 December	STAR 21 set new speed record of 264.1 m.p.h. (425.0 km/h) on Joetsu Shinkansen after earlier record of 261.0 m.p.h. (420.0 km/h) on 13 December.

1994

15 July	Two Series E1 MAX (Multiple-Amenity Express) sets entered service on the Tohoku and Joetsu Shinkansen – the world's first completely double-decked high-speed trains. JR-West commenced construction of Series 500 prototype, designed for speed of 186m.p.h. (300km/h).

1995

17 January	Great Hanshin Earthquake interrupted Shinkansen services through Kobe between Shin-Osaka and Himeji.
27 January	JR-Central's 300X experimental train delivered.
8 April	Through operation of Shinkansen services recommenced between Tokyo and Hakata.
April	Prototypes of JR-East's Series E2 and E3 trains completed for the Akita, Tohoku and Hokuriku Shinkansen.
25 May	Start of two years of trial running with '300X' between Maibara and Kyoto.
21 September	JR-Central's '300X' reached 220.0 m.p.h. (354.1 km/h) on Tokaido Line between Kyoto and Maibara.

1996

31 January	First Series 500 set completed for JR-West.
March	'300X' set undertakes running tests on Sanyo Shinkansen.
18 March	Ground-breaking ceremony at Yodogawa-ku for second Tokaido-Sanyo Shinkansen control centre.
25 March	Government permission given for construction of second terminal for Tokaido Shinkansen in Tokyo.
30 March	Tazawako Line closed for conversion to standard-gauge Shinkansen route between Morioka and Omagari.
1 April	Outstanding debts of defunct Japanese National Railways reach ¥27.6 trillion, presenting government with difficulties in covering it. Subsequent Cabinet decision that unpaid debts at the end of Fiscal Year 1997 be met by the public.
April	JR-West's Series 500 unit reaches 320 km/h (199 m.p.h.).
20 July	Provision of 'Ladies Only' toilets announced for Tohoku and Joetsu Shinkansen.
26 July	JR-Central's '300X' train reached new Japanese record of 443.0 km/h (275.3 m.p.h.) between Kyoto and Maibara, making it the second fastest train in the world after the French TGV No.325.
20 September	JR-West and JR-Central announced plans for Series N300 rolling-stock for through running on Tokaido and Sanyo Shinkansen. (Later to become Series 700). Series 700 prototype completed.
8 October	JR-West shares listed on Tokyo Stock Exchange.
29 October	Trial running began on JR-East's Hokuriku Shinkansen.
17 November	JR-East relocate Chuo Line viaduct north of Tokyo Central station to provide space for additional Shinkansen platform.
13 December	Track for Akita Shinkansen completed.
14 December	Trial runs start with JR-West's Series 500 Shinkansen between Osaka and Tokyo.

1997

21 February	JR-East announced plans to extend Yamagata Shinkansen to Shinjo by 2000.
22 March	Passenger services start on the JR-East's Akita Shinkansen, with schedules of 3 hours 49 minutes to Tokyo. Series 500 units begin passenger operation on Sanyo Shinkansen.
3 April	Running tests began on Yamanashi Maglev test track.
26 May	Ground-breaking ceremony for new station at Shinagawa to enable the operation of up to 15 JR-Central Shinkansen departures per hour from Tokyo.
12 July	19-storey Kyoto station building opened, the largest in Japan.
29 September	JR-East moves headquarters to near Shinjuku station in Tokyo. Site of former building sold to pay off part of JNR debt.
1 October	JR-East's Shinkansen link to Nagano opened, cutting time for *Asama* expresses from Tokyo by over half.
3 October	Series 700 Shinkansen train for JR-Central and JR-West unveiled.
8 October	JR-Central shares went on offer at four Stock Exchanges.

28 November	MLX01 Maglev train set world record speed for manned vehicle of 503 km/h (312.5 m.p.h.) on Yamanashi Test Track.
29 November	Maximum speed of Series 500 *Nozomi* Shinkansen increased to 300 km/h (186 m.p.h.) on Sanyo Shinkansen, cutting journey times by 15 minutes. Sets commence running through to Tokyo.
20 December	JR-East introduced Series E4 double-deck Shinkansen sets, with seats for 1634 passengers, primarily used on commuter services between Nasu Shiobara and Tokyo.
24 December	Unmanned MXL01 Maglev train reached new record of 550 km/h (341.8 m.p.h.), beating speed of 530km/h (329.9m.p.h.) attained on 12 December.

1998

7 February	Winter Olympic Games began at Nagano. During the 16-day event, 655 000 passengers travelled there by Shinkansen.
February–May	Series 700 prototype conducts running tests on Sanyo Shinkansen.
10 February	Former JNR Headquarters building in front of Tokyo Central Station sold at auction for ¥300.8 billion.
12 March	Japan's Ministry of Transport approved construction plans for three new Shinkansen Hachinohe-Shin-Amori (Tohoku Shinkansen) Nagano–Joetsu (Hokuriku Shinkansen) Funagoya–Shin-Yatsushiro (Kyushu Shinkansen)
18 March	JR-East Culture Foundation announced plans to restore part of former Shimbashi station to 1872 condition for Japanese Railway Settlement Corporation.
March	Installation of automatic ticket gates completed on Tokaido Shinkansen stations except Shin-Osaka.
5 April	Akashi Kaiko Bridge, the longest suspension type in the world, opened between Kobe and Awaji Island. Centre span is 1990 m (2177 yards) long.
11 June	Tests with two trains commenced on Yamanashi Maglev Test Line.
30 June	JR-Central reveal plans to build new 'Doctor Yellow' track-testing unit for Tokaido Shinkansen, based on Series 700 technology.
25 September	Announcement that one of the end cars of JR-East's STAR21 and JR-West's WIN350 were to be preserved at Technical Centre in Maibara.
6 October	JR-East celebrated the carrying of 1 billion Shinkansen passengers.
22 October	JNR Settlement Corporation disbanded. Outstanding work to be undertaken by Japan Railway Construction Public Corporation, and long-term debt of ¥27.7 trillion to be taken over by government.
30 November	Test run of gauge-changing train at Railway Technical Research Institute at Kokubunji, Tokyo.
8 December	Shinkansen journey times from Tokyo to Akita and Morioka reduced. Series E2 sets took over most of workings on Tohoku Shinkansen
16 December	JR-East agreed to build new station at Hoinjo City on Joetsu Shinkansen, the cost being met by the local community. Opening due in 2004.
17 December	Maglev trains pass successfully at combined speed of 966 km/h (600 m.p.h.) on Yamanashi Maglev Test Line.

1999

February	Tokaido Shinkansen Second General Control Centre completed at Osaka.
2 February	JR-Central agrees to pay additional ¥20.7 billion to help meet debt obligations of former JNR.
24 February	JR-East accepts extra share of JNR debt.
13 March	Series 700 Shinkansen enter service on *Nozomi* services between Tokyo and Hakata, at speeds of up to 285 km/h (177 m.p.h.).
14 April	Manned, 5-car maglev train reaches 552 km/h (343 m.p.h.) on Yamanashi Maglev Test line, beating previous records for manned and unmanned maglev.
28 May	JR-Central announced plans for automatic ATC system to be introduced on Tokaido Shinkansen in 2006 to enable faster recovery from delays, higher levels of safety, reliability and easier maintenance, with one-step braking curve.
September	Last of JR-Central's Series 0 units withdrawn from service.
October	All Series 100 trains with dining cars withdrawn from service. All through *Nozomi* services between Tokyo and Hakata being operated exclusively with Series 500 and 700 units.
4 December	JR-East extends mini-Shinkansen services from Yamagata to Shinjo. Two additional Series 400 trainsets introduced. Shinkansen services to Akita and Morioka accelerated with use of 275 km/h (171 m.p.h.) Series E2 trains.

2000

5 February	First female Shinkansen driver starts work on Tokaido Shinkansen.
March	All dining-car services withdrawn on the Tokaido and Sanyo Shinkansen.
July	The Tokaido Shinkansen receives two prestigious awards. The Institution of Electrical & Electronic Engineers honours the line as "An Electrical Engineering Milestone", and the American Society of Mechanical Engineers designates the railway as "A Landmark in Mechanical Engineering"

For those wanting further information on the history of Japanese Railways, there is now an excellent English-language book on the subject:

'A History of Japanese Railways 1872–1999', by Eiichi Aoki, Mitsuhide Imashiro, Shinichi Kato and Yasup Wakuda, published in 2000 by the East Japan Railway Culture Foundation. Available from Asahiya (London), Unit 34, Oriental City, 399 Edgware Road, London NW9 0JJ, tel: 0208-200-0039, fax 0208-200-8872.

A night view of the Shinkansen platforms at Tokyo station in March 1997.

Mikio Miura

Glossary and Abbreviations

Aoba	'Green Leaves'. The name of the stopping trains on the Tohoku Shinkansen.
Asahi	'Morning Sun'. The name of the limited-stop trains on the Joetsu Shinkansen.
Asama	An active volcano, Mount Asama, located near Karuizawa on the Nagano Shinkansen. The name of the limited-stop trains between Tokyo and Nagano.
ATC	Automatic Train Control.
ATP	Automatic Train Protection, the UK term for a signalling system which prevents signals being over-run by the driver. The Japanese ATS fulfils such a role.
BR	British Rail, the unified national railway system in the UK before privatisation.
COMTRAC	Computer-Aided Traffic Control system.
EMU	Electric multiple-unit train.
Hikari	'Light'. The name of the original limited-stop trains between Tokyo and Osaka, and still used for many present-day workings.
'Japanese-gauge'	Railway tracks with a gap of 3feet 6inches (1,067mm) between the rails. This was the gauge used on the majority of the JNR system, but other railways in the country have used tracks of other gauges.
JNR	Japanese National Railways.
JR	Japan Railways (Group), the current way of referring to the lines operated by the former JNR.
JR-C	Central Japan Railway.
JR-E	East Japan Railway.
JR-W	West Japan Railway.
Kodama	'Echo'. The name of the stopping trains on the Tokaido and Sanyo Shinkansen.
Komachi	A famous female poet from Akita in the Heinan period. The name of the 'Mini-Shinkansen' services between Morioka and Akita.
MAX	Multi-Amenity Express, JR-E's double-deck Shinkansen trains.
Nasuno	A tableland which forms part of the northern Tokyo commuter area. The name of Tohoku Shinkansen trains which start or finish at Nasu-Shiobara station.
NATM	New Austrian Tunnelling Method. An old technique which was renamed in the 1970s after being used extensively for the construction of the Vienna Metro. After removing a few feet of ground with mechanical picks, the periphery is reinforced and covered with steel netting on to which special concrete is sprayed. At a later stage a conventional reinforced-concrete lining may be cast inside it.
Nozomi	'Hope'. The name of the fastest trains on the Tokaido and Sanyo Shinkansen.
SNCF	*Société Nationale de Chemins de fer Français*, the nationalised French main-line railway system.
Standard-gauge	Railway tracks with a gap of 4ft 8½in (1,435mm) between the rails.
Tanigawa	Mount Tanigawa, notable for its difficult climbing, located above Dai Shimizu Tunnel on the Joetsu Shinkansen. The name of the all-stations Shinkansen trains between Tokyo and Echigo-Yuzawa.
TGV	*Trains à Grande Vitesse*, the SNCF high-speed trains.
Toki	'Crested Ibis'. The name of the stopping trains on the Joetsu Shinkansen.
Tsubasa	'Wings'.The name of the 'Mini-Shinkansen' trains running between Tokyo and Yamagata.
VVVF	Variable-Voltage, Variable-Frequency, describing the type of power system used to control the output of the asynchronous alternating-current traction motors used on the latest designs of rolling stock.
Yamabiko	'Mountain Echo'. The name of the limited-stop trains on the Tohoku Shinkansen.

APPENDIX I

Conversion Factors

Mile	(mile)	0.621	I	1.609	Kilometre	(km)
Foot	(ft)	3.281	I	0.305	Metre	(m)
Yard	(yd)	1.094	I	0.914	Metre	(m)
Inch	(in)	0.039	I	25.4	Millimetre	(mm)
Imperial Gallon	(gal)	0.220	I	4.546	Litre	(l)
Imperial Gallon	(gal)	0.833	I	1.201	US Gallon	(US gal)
Imperial Ton	(ton)	0.984	I	1.016	Metric Tonne	(t)
Imperial Ton	(ton)	0.833	I	1.120	US Ton	(US ton)
Pound	(lb)	2.205	I	0.454	Kilogram	(kg)
Horsepower	(hp)	1.340	I	0.746	Kilowatt	(kW)
Miles per Hour	(mph)	1.152	I	0.868	Knot	(kt)
Pound Force	(lbf)	0.2248	I	4.448	Newton	(N)

The table should be read from the centre column outwards. For example, I kilometre equals 0.621 miles, while I mile equals 1.609 kilometres.

APPENDIX 2

Approximate rates of exchange between UK Sterling, Japanese ¥en and US Dollars, 1960–2000

Exchange Rates
£1 Sterling equalled

Year	Japanese ¥en	US Dollars
1960	1010	2.80
1965	1010	2.80
1970	860	2.40
1975	720	2.30
1980	530	2.20
1985	290	1.20
1990	240	1.70
1995	160	1.60
2000	170	1.62

The figures are rounded to the nearest 10 ¥en and 10 cents US, and are for the beginning of the year concerned.

UK Inflation Factors
The value in the year shown was approximately equivalent to one Pound Sterling in 2000

Year	Equivalent in 2000 (GBP)
1964	11.84
1967	10.56
1970	9.02
1975	4.90
1980	2.49
1985	1.76
1990	1.32
1995	1.11

A Shinkansen for all Seasons

SPRING

Left: On a sunny day in cherry-blossom time, a *Nozomi* speeds across the River Tama.

SUMMER

Below left: In the summer after-glow, a *Nozami* from Hakata to Tokyo passes the marina at Lake Hamana.

AUTUMN

Right: The colours of the trees indicate the season as a *Tsubasa* emerges from Matsukawa Tunnel to cross a lofty viaduct near Itaya Summit on the Yamagata line.

WINTER

Below: Snow blankets Tokyo as a *Nozomi*, bound for Hakata, makes its way past the suburban station at Shinagawa.

Mikio Miura (4)

Biographies

PETER SEMMENS is a Cornishman who has travelled widely by rail throughout the world. For more than 40 years he has been known for his numerous contributions to railway literature, and since 1981 he has been the author of the Railway Magazine's long-running 'Practice & Performance' column. He became the publication's Chief Correspondent in 1990. From 1974 until 1987 he was the first Assistant Keeper at the National Railway Museum in York. He is Vice-President of the Stephenson Locomotive Society and Hon. President of the Railway Performance Society.

MIKIO MIURA comes from Tokyo. For many years he has been travelling and photographing in Japan and overseas, and has built up an enviable world train library of photographs. After a long career in the Central Bank of Japan he founded Galerie 'Trains du Monde' in Tokyo in 1991, where railway- and travel-oriented exhibitions are shown. He has co-authored, edited and illustrated many books and magazines, specialising in those describing high-speed trains.

FURTHER COPIES OF THIS BOOK

Further copies of this book can be obtained from the publishers PLATFORM 5 PUBLISHING LIMITED, 3 Wyvern House, Sark Road, SHEFFIELD, S2 4HG, ENGLAND, price £22.50 plus postage and packing at 10% (UK – 2nd Class), 20% (Europe – via Airmail), 30% (Rest of the World – via Air Freight), 50% (Rest of the World – via Airmail). Payment by Sterling cheque (drawn on a UK bank), Eurocheque or credit card (MasterCard or Visa).

Telephone: +44 (0) 114 255 8000   Fax: +44 (0) 114 255 2471

Platform 5 Publishing are publishers of high quality British and European railway rolling stock guides and specialists in Light Rail Transit.

Publishers of 'TODAY'S RAILWAYS – THE PAN-EUROPEAN RAILWAY MAGAZINE' and 'LIGHT RAIL REVIEW'.